Healthy
Stories

Dedicated to the limited
number of Public Health
Servants and to the vast
number of those who serve
Public Health.

And to the Editor's families.

ISBN: 0-615-2063450995
Copyright 2008
Printed on recycled paper.
Printed in the United States of America.

Healthy Stories

Sharing Our
Health Department Stories
With the World

Morton Laitner
Editor-in-Chief

Heather Beaton

Tracie L. Dickerson

Amy Tejirian

Roland R. Pierre

Ninfa Urdaneta

J.D. Shingles

Frederick Villari

Michael Cover

Our Mission

To promote and protect the health of people through
educational stories about prevention, preparedness, and wellness.

Our Vision

To create a world-wide publication promoting the values
of Public Health Departments and the health of our communities.

Our Goals

To delight our readers:

Making them laugh, cry, and ponder
the message conveyed in each vignette;

Teaching them how Health Departments affect their lives;

Educating them on how to improve their health;

Instructing them that humorous stories make the best medicine;
and,

Coaching story-telling methodology as the principal way
to get Health Department messages understood
and remembered by the general public;

Inspiring them through memorializing how
we care and provide quality health services.

Healthy Stories

FOREWORD
From the Administrator of the Miami-Dade County Health Department

Our Health Department vision is to be a world-class public health system. Healthy Stories leads us on this journey.

Sharing our stories with the world is this year's goal of Healthy Stories. I am proud to acknowledge our success. Healthy Stories has inspired readers across the United States in California, Texas, Louisiana, Kansas and New York and across the globe in the United Kingdom, Israel, Venezuela and Canada.

When I received my copy of Healthy Stories 2007, I was so proud of this publication that I framed the book launching poster and hung it in my office. These stories represent our Health Department history. These stories represent what we are about: caring, creativity, fun-loving and most of all, our desire to protect the health of our community.

Healthy Stories is an innovative marketing tool we are using with our internal and external customers. We have focused our publication by utilizing stories concerning: smoking cessation, vaccinations, chronic disease, AIDS and STD prevention, alcohol abuse, environmental health, tuberculosis control, hand washing and communicable disease. This year, the editors are giving our readers an added bonus by including seven stories from Healthy Stories 2007 that have been translated into Spanish and Creole.

I hope you enjoy Healthy Stories 2008 as much as I did. I know these anecdotes will inspire and educate you about what everyday life is like in a County Health Department.

Lillian Rivera,
R.N., M.S.N., Ph.D.

Introduction

It has been an exciting year since the publication of our first edition of Healthy Stories. In this edition, we have a number of firsts: a love story, a tragedy, a prose poem and an original art work.

Marketing

Healthy Stories was published on eleven (11) websites, including the Miami-Dade County Department of Health site where you can still view the 2007 edition.

Other websites that published our book included the Centers for Disease Control and Prevention Public Health News, the United States Army Center for Health Promotion and Preventative Medicine Health Information Operations, and the following reference cites, Wikipedia, Reference.com, Medlibrary.org and Uberpedia.org and some fun sites that surprised us: Top40-charts, videoinside.org and nosmut.com.

We wrote and released our first press kits. We created partnerships with the City of Coral Springs Radio and Television Division, CityTV 25 and CityRadio 1670 AM and have given our Creole stories to Planet Radio 1580 AM. We found interested readers at health fairs and distributed copies to our community partners, physician's offices and to all fifty public health state associations as well as the Southern Health Association.

Community Service

After reading a recent article in the May 2008 edition of The Writer, discussing a report "entitled To Read or not to Read, (online at www.nea.gov/research/researchreports_chrono.html), the article reveal[ed] Americans are reading less and describes how our culture and economy are negatively impacted by the nations diminishing reading habits" It further states, "with today's jobs demanding employees skilled at handling and analyzing data, we're in danger of falling short of those needs." In order to promote literacy in our workforce and the sharing of our stories with everyone, we donated

Healthy Stories 2007 to Read for Health, a Florida Department of Health website committed to improve the health and welfare of Florida citizens through reading. The editors also gave all fifty-three public libraries in Miami-Dade County, Florida a copy of Healthy Stories for their patrons.

We have lectured to over sixty prisoners at the Miami-Dade County Department of Corrections Facility, and each prisoner received a copy of Healthy Stories.

Education

We have lectured on Healthy Stories at the Stempel School of Public Health at Florida International University. We have commenced a working relationship with the University of Miami Department of Ethics.

We have been honored to give the Brumback Lecture on the subject of Healthy Stories at the Florida Public Health Association, at which every member in attendance of the lecture was given a copy as a part of their take away bags. The most rewarding aspect of the publication has been our readers' comments and positive feedback.

Our stories have been accepted, published and highly ranked by Helium.com. Helium is a website devoted to the art of writing.

Wondrous Occurrences
- Discussing with a Health Department Employee of the Muslim faith his religious obligations and how when he read our story "Speak Softly and Carry a Big Stick" he realized the effect of how a personal quarantine would affect his ability to pray on a daily basis.
- Seeing how sixty prisoners enjoyed the stories when we lectured to them as a part of Operation Re-entry (after serving up to twenty-five years in the Florida Department of Corrections Facility).
- Watching a non-public health reader while she sat deeply immersed reading the stories, and then she commented on how much joy and satisfaction they gave her.
- Remembering when an editor gave the book to his wife to read, she enjoyed the book so much she commented that she loved

the stories, but felt the book was a little too thin, her indirect way of asking for more stories.

- Listening to how mothers and grandmothers related to "Triplets on the Plane" and wrote us about their own experience with their multiple children.
- Hearing one reader call our stories "Treasures."
- Feeling an enormous sense of pride when readers asked for their copies of the book to be autographed.

The Editors

WINNER OF THE
2008 BEST STORY COMPETITION

A Survivor's Love Story

By John Holmes,
Environmental Health Director,
Putnam County Health Department

Dedicated to Marianne

I walked into the Key West Women Infants and Children (WIC) office with tears running down my cheeks. "Marianne is not coming," I told my friend. I was trying to explain while holding back the sobs which were tearing at my heart. "I just talked to her on the phone; she decided not to come. We planned this for almost two years. Now it is completely over. She asked me to ship her belongings back to her. The worst part is she has asked I not contact her anymore!"

Marianne is the love of my life. We met at Rochester Institute of Technology in New York where we lived in the same campus building. My wife left me shortly after school started. Marianne was dealing with a failing marriage of her own. It all started innocently. I would see her outside reading or just relaxing under a tree after work. We would talk casually about school and our past. Marianne is Dutch. She lived in the United States for almost 30 years. We talked about places we had both visited. Time with Marianne made my grueling class schedule almost bearable. We walked from campus housing to the health center following streets and a shortcut through the woods directly behind the campus.

Almost imperceptibly, we moved emotionally closer. Neither of us knew what was happening. We started holding hands and would say goodbye with a hug. Marianne was invited to an awards banquet;

she asked me to accompany her. It was a cool misty evening outside the Eastman House in Rochester that night. We sat through the ceremony which was followed by a dinner with music and dancing. We were enjoying the evening and decided to step outside for some fresh air. The mist had changed to a light drizzle so we decided to sit near a grape arbor – an overhead trellis on which grape vines grow. We sat next to each other to stay warm. Mellowed on wine we found ourselves in a romantic atmosphere. I turned to Marianne, looking into her kaleidoscope eyes and said, "I love you." She looked at me and replied, "ik houd van jou," which is Dutch for I love you. My heart was beating in my throat and my head was pounding. I then said to Marianne, "I want us to be together forever." Marianne replied, "I have felt the same way for quite awhile."

Our love continued to grow and soon we decided to get married. There were many difficulties to overcome, but it was inevitable we would be together.

I was in a state of shock as I was sitting in the chair in the WIC office trembling with a chill. My mind was disconnected from my body. My thoughts were only of Marianne. Now what would I do? My friend tried to console me, but I was too devastated to comprehend what had just happened. I contacted my supervisor and explained that I was not feeling well and needed to go home for the rest of the day.

At home, I felt empty. I sat in disbelief at my situation. Slowly I collected Marianne's personal belongings for shipment. It took several days to complete what should have taken a few hours. Each item held a memory. I was packing and shipping my love and dreams. It was the most difficult task I had ever done. As my dreams where being weighed and tagged for shipment, I decided that I was not going to fall to pieces. I was going to lose myself in my work. I was going to work so hard that I would not have time to think about Marianne. I did not know that my future would bring the most difficult time of my life. In my pain of losing Marianne, I could not have comprehended there would be a time in my near future when I would have a brush with the Angel of Death.

Work became my obsession. Double-duty workloads did not give me the peace I craved. The harder I tried, the more troubled I became. It did not make sense – the way Marianne ended our plans.

I just could not accept it. I thought that if I could work myself to exhaustion, I could at least escape her when I slept. Sleep was fitful. I created a business so I would have additional work to fill my nights and weekends and give me extra money to help solve my growing financial crisis.

My financial crisis began when I was in my forties with a family and had injured my back. I decided that the only way I would be able to support my family was to earn a college degree. I had over-estimated what my market value would be when I graduated. This led me to believe that I would be able to repay my massive student loans. My debt load upon graduation was beyond my ability to pay. I hoped the additional income from the side business would solve my problems. First, it would distract me from the painful end of my relationship with Marianne and, second, it would help pay-off my debts. After several months, it was obvious that my debt coupled with the high cost of living in The Keys was unmanageable. I decided to take the most humiliating solution to my financial problems and I filed for bankruptcy. I had become a bankrupt, broken-hearted loser. I guessed by now that maybe Marianne was right. She somehow sensed that I was really a loser and I was beginning to believe it.

Bankruptcy eliminated much of my debt, but not all. I still had to pay back my student loans, yet it did help some. I needed to either get a raise or a promotion. I realized that without one or the other my career would soon be over and I would need to seek other employment.

My opportunity came quickly when my supervisor decided to retire unexpectedly. I was the next senior inspector in the office and I had been through several staff turnovers already. Now was my time to be rewarded for my loyalty and hard work. I felt a buoyancy that helped push my problems to the background. I looked forward to going to work again. I almost smiled again, something I had not done in a long time. I secretly thought to myself: just wait Marianne; you will see that I am not a loser. The day of the interview proved again that, yes, I am a loser. I was now a bankrupt, rejected loser.

I was devastated at this new loss. I realized I had only one avenue to follow – leave the Keys. I decided to transfer to another health department.

My search did not take long. I was offered a job in a small rural county in the northeast part of the state. I would be promoted and the cost of living was substantially less. This was the best news I had in many years. I accepted the job and made plans to transfer. I finished all my open cases and left for my new life. I had no idea where I would live or what it would cost. All I cared about was a new beginning.

When I arrived, the first place I went was to a motel to make plans to stay for several weeks until I could find someplace to live. It did not take long. One of my co-workers knew a person who had a place to rent. I checked it out and took it. I finally had a new home.

Time passed quickly and I became a part of the team immediately. I needed some retraining because there are many differences in Environmental Health between the Keys and where I was now working. I learned quickly and settled down to live my new life. Marianne was always with me. I thought about her everyday. Time had dulled the pain, but the memories were still vivid. I did not talk to anyone about her, but I think that sometimes I seemed distracted with something.

A year and a half later, I was driving between inspections with a colleague. I told her I was having a terrible pain in the middle of my back and I needed to stop to walk it off. We stopped and it went away after quite some time. I had an annual physical scheduled in a couple days and made a mental note to tell my doctor about it.

I took the day off for my physical and was there 15 minutes early (I operate on Lombardy time). The receptionist took my information and put me in the exam room where I waited for the doctor. When he arrived, we had the usual discussion and I told him about the pain in my back. He ran an EKG and after examining the results, told me I had experienced a heart attack and needed to have a stress test immediately. I told him that I did not have time for one right now, but I would have one when I returned from a trip later that week. I had planned to help drive my friend's car to Phoenix and fly back. I was only going to be gone a few days. The doctor said he would not recommend the trip and said it was imperative that I get the test. I relented and agreed to have the test the next day. Again I arrived 15 minutes early, ready to put this all behind me. Besides, I was okay and the doctor was just being overly cautious.

The test went quickly. It was a thallium treadmill test. I had a little trouble completing the treadmill part, but I was just out of shape. The cardiologist returned with the results and told me it indicated a major blockage. He said I should have an angiogram immediately. I told him thanks, but no thanks; I had a trip to go on and would have it done when I returned. He told me that I may not make it back, that the heart attack I experienced would probably be my only warning. The next one would in all likelihood be major if not fatal. Again, I agreed to have the test and it was scheduled for the next day. I completed the test and the results showed that I needed open heart surgery as soon as possible. I was taken from the exam area to an ambulance where I was transferred to a hospital in Jacksonville for surgery the next day. Marianne really had broken my heart.

I awoke with a pipe in my throat! I could not swallow and was in a panic. I wanted the pipe out right now. The nurse told me I needed to calm down and it would be removed as soon as possible. They needed to leave the pipe there so I would continue to breathe in case there was a problem. Eventually, the pipe was removed and I was able to calm down. I was returned to intensive care for recovery. When the doctors decided I was doing fine, they would return me to the recovery area and finally to my room. I was heavily sedated and not able to comprehend anything, but after several days in intensive care, I figured there was something wrong. I asked questions and realized that all was not right. There was trouble in the operating room, my heart did not start up right away and my abdominal organs were not working properly. My kidneys were not working. In other words, I was slowly dying and nobody knew what to do. I wished I could say goodbye to Marianne. I wanted her to lie next to me so I could hold her as I slipped away. I wanted my last words to be, "I love you." Later that night I awoke in a morphine induced state of disillusionment and self-pity. I turned to buzz the on duty nurse and as I watched the door, suddenly, I envisioned a faceless-dark-hooded figure. I remember wondering if the grim reaper had come to harvest my soul.

After five days, I still was not recovering well enough, so they decided to do a complete CAT scan of my chest and abdomen. It was a cold January night when they took me for the test. I was shivering uncontrollably. They rolled me into the scan room and took so many scans I should have glowed in the dark. I was returned to my room to wait for the results the next day. When my doctor came to my room, he was not alone. He brought an oncologist. He said they had found a large tumor near my kidney and it would need to be removed as soon as I was well enough to withstand the trauma. The doctor said that the tumor was resting on a large artery causing a condition called Deep Vein Thrombosis (DVT) which is essentially an accumulation of clots in my leg. This could lead to any number of serious, if not fatal, complications. The one positive fact in all this gloom was that the tumor was encapsulated which essentially gave me more time, but I could not wait forever.

For whatever reason, I started to recover shortly after the CAT scans and was returned to my room where I remained for an additional 10 days. I continued to improve in most respects, but was having trouble walking. The nurse had me up several times a day walking the halls and finally I was well enough to go home to heal from my heart surgery.

I was recovering at home and trying not to worry about the upcoming surgery. My friend Diane was staying with me as a live-in nurse. She went through the ringer with me. I could not sleep right; would not eat. Nothing tasted like it was worth eating. About three weeks after I was home, I fell ill again and returned to the hospital. It seemed my kidneys were failing again. I do not know what happened, only that I eventually returned home to continue my recovery and try to gain enough strength to have the next surgery. I wondered if Marianne realized just how much I loved her and how badly she broke my heart.

About two months after the bypass surgery I returned to the hospital to have the cancer removed. The tumor was so large it had to be removed from the front. While the surgery was excessively invasive, there were no complications. I started to recover almost immediately and within ten days returned home. I continued my slow recovery. Diane needed to leave to take care of some family business, so a co-worker at the health department said I could stay with him and his wife until I could care for myself. That amounted to three weeks. I was now in my home able to get around, but my recovery was not progressing well. I did not have the spirit to go on. I wondered if it was all worth it. I just didn't care. I had been through so many heartaches, so many disappointments; now I was a complete physical mess! Why was I being beat-down so bad? I could not find a reason to continue or to try to get well.

I took a road trip to visit my parents who lived about 50 miles away. I was not sure I could drive that far, but decided to try. I arrived at my parent's home exhausted from the drive. I went inside, had a drink of water and went to the spare bedroom to take a nap. When I awoke, mom had cooked a meal and was waiting for me. We talked and I told them about how lucky I was to be alive. After the meal, my mother brought me a letter from "an old friend of mine" that had arrived a couple of days earlier. I was stunned to find it was from Marianne! She wrote that she was trying to find me. She wanted to apologize for the way our relationship ended. Marianne enclosed all her contact information so I could find her if I wanted.

The anger rose in my throat. It was blocked by my memories of our love. I wanted to yell at her and hold her tight at the same time. I realized I was stomping around in my parent's home and decided to sit in an effort to calm down. I read the letter repeatedly trying to decipher what she might really be saying. I placed the letter in my pocket until I returned home. I read, re-read, and re-re-read and still could not get it out of my head that there was more-than-what-met-the-eye. That same night I replied to her letter in which I told her about moving and the promotion. I wrote that I was happy with my life. I had a new friend who was French and cared for me. She stayed with me during my health issues. I went on and on. I wanted Marianne to know that I did not need her anymore. I even signed the letter "sincerely." The one time in my life when it meant the most, my anger overruled my heart. I sent the letter and that was that.

Two days later I received a phone call. The Caller-ID showed it was Marianne! I let it ring several times and reluctantly answered it. I heard her voice and all my anger melted and turned to tears. I knew that I still loved her as if nothing had ever happened. Marianne apologized for what had happened. She reminded me that her mother was gravely ill at the time she was to come to me and passed away shortly after that. I could hear her softly crying on the phone when she said she never stopped loving me. She expressed that she always believed one day we would be together. As she continued, I realized she never had abandoned me. Marianne had entrusted me with her heart. She never took it back. I asked her to forgive me for doubting her love. We must have talked for hours. When we realized that we had talked long enough, I asked what she wanted to do now. Could we meet somehow? She told me she had just gone through cancer surgery herself and could not travel very far. We decided to meet in Valdosta, Georgia.

A couple of weeks later we met. To see the two of us together one would have been shocked. I could not get out of my truck by myself. Marianne had lost so much weight that I might have missed her on the street. We were about as pathetic as two people could be. Marianne helped me out of my truck. We hugged, we kissed and we knew we would be together for the rest of our lives.

We met in Valdosta a couple more times. My recovery was slowly improving. We were making our plans for our future together. On our last trip we visited San Mateo, Florida, and looked at a house to purchase. Marianne thought it was ugly until I told her how I envisioned our home. When we went inside she found the house welcoming. I knew we would live there soon. We went back to the motel and decided to make an offer. We moved in three months later.

Although my health problems were not over, I knew everything would be fine. Shortly before we moved into our home, I developed a condition that required a cervical fusion. I had surgery without any problems and felt as if I could have jumped off the operating table and gone home. Marianne was at my side the whole time, and that was all that mattered. Marianne was taking a break from her life to recover also. She was gaining weight and smiling again. I was glad she was able to recover with me.

Guess what? Three months later I had surgery again; I had my gallbladder removed! Fifteen months: four surgeries, two mended hearts.

Now as I walk into the WIC office, tears of joy run down my face as I tell Diane the rest of the story. Marianne and I are happily married. I have been promoted to senior management. Marianne has become an American citizen. Both of us have fully recovered and are cancer free for over five years.

WE AND OUR LOVE HAVE SURVIVED.

The Band-Aid

By Tracie L. Dickerson

O ver my summer vacation I discovered just how important a band-aid could be. Working for the Health Department and attending all of the extra trainings has made me more prepared for minor emergencies. Before embarking on a 3,000 mile journey through Nevada, California, Arizona and Utah, I decided that I should get some water and other provisions, considering the sweltering 117 degrees it was outside. I went to the front desk the evening before to get two important things, 1. the directions to the local mega-mart and 2. the directions to Death Valley National Park.

As the Concierge was looking for my directions a slightly panicked and very frantic person ran up to the counter. She exclaimed, "Someone has been hurt. It's not too bad but he may need stitches. I am a nurse and I need a butterfly band-aid." The concierge looks to me and asks again where I was planning to travel to.

I was perplexed. A paying guest took precedence over a minor emergency! I looked at this nicely dressed woman and looked back at the front desk help. Understanding the needs of a bleeding person that may need stitches came well before my directions to Death Valley, I told the front desk person to find the first aid kit.

I learned long ago that the donut-glazed-over eyes with the blank-faced stare is never something you want to see from a person who is supposed to help you. To my utter shock and surprise the clerk walked away and went to the back for what seemed like an eternity.

I spoke with the frazzled woman to help her calm down a bit. I discovered that her boyfriend was the bass player in a band that was playing at the hotel bar. Some equipment fell and he had a two inch gash on his forehead. Cancelling the concert was not an option, but forehead wounds bleed like crazy and she needed to do something quickly.

We waited a few more moments for the clerk to return. "I am sorry miss, but we don't have a first aid kit." Realizing that the moment needed some decisive action, I switched into lawyer mode. "You mean the front desk does not have a first-aid kit?" He responded with a "Yes." "Does housekeeping have a first aid kit?" "No". "Do the employees have a first aid kit?" "No." "If you fell and hurt yourself who would you call?" "Security."

Aha! So security was the answer to getting the person help. "So security might have a band-aid?"

"Yes. Some of the guards have been EMT trained."

"Great," I said, "you call security and have them report to the café with the band-aids."

In an abundance of caution, I always carry a small first aid kit with me when I travel. I have used it only once, but I feel better knowing it is there. I looked at the woman and said, "I have a first-aid kit in my room. It is small, but at least it is something. I will meet you at the café." Dashing up to my room, I went over to my carry on and after a few seconds of searching I found my trusty kit. I went back downstairs and on the way saw the security guard that had been dispatched with his one band-aid.

The security guard saw me and told me to go back to my room. I headed back toward the elevator, but then my Health Department trainings kicked in. I knew what I needed to do. At the very least I needed to find the woman and let her know that I had come back. I needed to make sure that I was no longer a necessary part of the equation!

After three times through the concepts of Incident Command training and the importance of making sure I was not needed, Security let me into the Club/Café. Within seconds I found the woman. She was still in distress! The Security Guard was unable to help her boyfriend, who was now on stage playing. The large (still bleeding) gash on his head was mostly covered by a folded napkin sandwiched in by a large hat.

When I handed over my first-aid kit complete with alcohol swabs and butterfly band-aids, I thought this woman was going to cry. She gave me a huge hug, bought me a drink and invited me to stay as a guest of the band for the rest of the night. It makes me laugh to think that I was a band-aid for the evening! ☼

The Greatest Gift

By Mort Laitner

My office phone rang six times before I picked up the receiver. I heard my mother's familiar voice. Something was wrong. Her words trembled, "Son, I got my test results. My doctor said I have pancreatic cancer!" My heart fell to the floor. Fear paralyzed my body. Tears formed in my eyes then rolled down my face. I tasted salt as these tears ran onto my lips.

"Mom, you'll be okay. You'll beat it. You are a survivor." What else could I say? The words left my mouth in a quiver. "I'll see you tonight. We'll work on a plan. I'll start researching the disease. I love you, good bye."

As I hung up the phone, I realized I knew absolutely nothing about pancreatic cancer. Immediately, I started an internet search. I read twenty sites in two hours. What I learned was not encouraging. In article after article, one number kept hitting me – six. Each site said that a person diagnosed with pancreatic cancer had only 6 months left to live. I studied the experimental treatments; all of them were a million to one.

My mother and I visited Baptist Hospital for her weekly chemotherapy. Mom was willing to be a human guinea pig in exchange for additional days on earth. I became her chauffeur, her entertainer and her cheerer-upper. While the injected chemo flowed into her veins, I read her stories. We reminisced about the good old days with our family and friends.

Mom lived on hope. She believed as a survivor that she could fight any disease and win. After three months of chemo, Mom scheduled her oncologist appointment. We would learn if the therapy was working. We took our usual drive to Baptist, silently praying for the success of the experimental therapy. As I looked at my mother sitting in the doctor's waiting room, she looked nervous but extremely hopeful. The young oncologist called us into his office and stood as he matter-of-factly looked at my mother and said, "Sorry, the experimental treatment failed." He then followed, "There is nothing else we can do to extend your life." I felt a hard fist punch into my solar plexus. The air was knocked out of my body. I looked at my mom's face. She held back her tears but she aged ten years in front of my eyes. Mom's hope had vanished. As I left the doctor's office and walked through the hospital to get to the garage, I cried uncontrollably. I did not care if anyone noticed. I pulled myself together by the time I drove to the front of the hospital to pick up Mom. We silently drove back to her home, each of us wondering why our prayers went unanswered.

I watched my mother deteriorate.

I had studied, "On Death and Dying" during the early days of the AIDS crisis. I decided to reread Kübler-Ross's classic. I watched as Mom journeyed through each of the five stages of loss – denial, anger, bargaining, depression, and, finally, acceptance.

As the cancer shriveled up my mother, my sister and I were advised to bring in a hospice worker. This angel of mercy gave us the comfort and assurance that we would survive this ordeal. My sister and I decided to rotate nights taking care of Mom. The night before my mother passed away, she suffered terribly. The pain caused angry words to be spewed at my sister. The next morning, I heard about the horrible night and was thankful that I was spared listening to my mother's agony. The doctor ordered an increase in morphine drops to numb the pain and to put Mom on a no-food-or-liquid regime. The hospice worker opined, "I think this will be your mother's last day with us." I calculated the dates, exactly six months from that fateful telephone call. That night I held Mom's hands in mine. Trembling, I said, "I'm going to miss you so much. Say hi to Dad for me. I love you." And my mom uttered her last three words, "I love you." Within an hour Mom passed away. My sister and I cried like abandoned orphans.

Eight years have passed since the death watch. I think of Mom on a daily basis, realizing that her parting words were the greatest gift she ever gave me. ☼

Many Healthy Stories readers have asked what response we received from the "Greatest Gift" story, here it is.

A Rivulet of Tears

By our Readers

The e-mails flowed in like a gentle stream rolling down a hill.
The story had hit a nerve, the optic nerve to be exact.
I remembered crying as I wrote it. Was it too personal to divulge?
Now others were sharing their perceptions as well as their grief.

The story is a moving narrative of a painful chapter in life.
As I read it, I remembered my mom's last days, our last word together. We each said, 'I love you.'

Tears of love

The trickling continued, "Not a day goes by when I do not think about my mother…My old habit of calling her to say I'm OK…A moment I want to share with Mom and then remember I can't. However, I do feel her presence. She stays with me for as long as I need her. I never feel alone."

Tears of togetherness

A note from my sister, "Thanks for the morning cry.
Every day I think of Mom."

Tears of remembrance

The next e-mail said it in just three words, "I cried too."

Tears of understanding

As I walked down the hall, a coworker approached me and said, "I
loved the story and to my astonishment, I uncontrollably wept in
my cubicle."

Tears of release

"The story brought me to tears, and it has reminded me how deep
the love of a son is. That's beautiful."

Tears of family

"I do not know what to say. My mom passed away a year ago. I can
not describe my agony. I'm not ashamed to say, 'I cried and even
screamed.' I thank God for the time we had together."

Tears of thanks

"I'm a cancer survivor. The story meant so much to me."

Tears of survival

"My mother recently died and I am still recovering."

Tears of recovery

"I felt your sadness ...and dread the day I will have to miss
my mom."

Tears of dread

The final e-mail was heartfelt. "A son never forgets..."

Tears

Physician, HEAL THYSELF

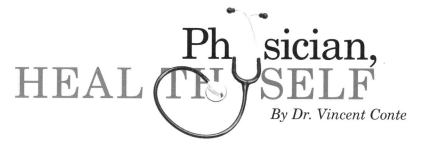

By Dr. Vincent Conte

I t started as a slight nagging ache in my lower back that just wouldn't go away. Advil made it better, but still the ache would return. It worsened over the next two months until finally I stopped a neurologist colleague of mine in the hospital hallway and told him about it. He wrote me a prescription for a CAT scan and instructed me to have the results sent to his office.

The day came for my scan. It was a beautiful, sunny Wednesday. I had my scan - one, two, three. Because I am a physician, I asked if I could read the scan on the spot with the radiologist. I was told that the radiologist, who also was a friend, was reading the scans from the main hospital today, but if I left my number, they would have her call me.

About twenty minutes later as I pulled into the Publix parking lot, my phone rang and the caller ID showed Baptist Hospital. I knew it was my radiologist with the results. I answered, "Hello. What could you see?" It turned out that I had a slightly herniated disc[1] in my lower back which accounted for the pain.

BUT, then came the shocker of my life. "Vince, I also see something suspicious in your left kidney and the way it lights up with the contrast. I hate to say, but I think it's Renal Cell Cancer." My world came to a screeching halt, and time seemed to stand still. I am a doctor. I'm not supposed to get cancer. In fact, I help cure it, so this can't be happening. A million thoughts went racing through my head and then her voice brought me back to reality. "It looks like its about 2.5 centimeters and looks partially cystic[2], but I am pretty sure it's cancer." Again, THAT word! CANCER. Impossible! It can't be in ME. I asked her, "Are you sure?" She replied, "I would bet my career on it." She asked me if I knew a good urologist, which

---

1 http://www.webmd.com/back-pain/tc/herniated-disc-topic-overview
2 http://en.wikipedia.org/wiki/Renal_cell_carcinoma

I did. She would forward a copy of my films to his office and told me I should go see him as soon as possible. I thanked her, still feeling it was all a bad dream.

I sat in my car for what seemed like an hour. My kids. My wife. MY LIFE. "What is going to happen? No, wait, calm down. It may not be a death sentence. Maybe it got caught early and I can beat this thing. Yep, I'll BET I CAN BEAT IT! Oh no, what if I can't?" These thoughts kept running through my head. I had seen countless patients with cancer come to the operating room. Some survive their ordeal and some don't. "Which would I be?" Then it really hit me and tears welled up in my eyes.

Cancer, the dreaded "C" word, and it was growing inside of me.

I immediately called my urologist and told his office that I needed to talk to him right away. He was in surgery. I asked where and placed a call to the operating room. I told the nurse that I urgently needed to speak to him. When he answered, I explained everything and asked when he could take this thing out of me. He tried his best to calm me down, and his words helped. "At 2.5 centimeters, you have a great chance of living a long, normal life. The odds change when it reaches 4 centimeters. Then things can be bad. But at 2.5 centimeters, it will be all OK, so calm down. Call my office and come see me this afternoon after I finish surgery." I promptly called the office and made the appointment for 3:00 pm. It was only 12:30 pm. What would I do for the next 2.5 hours? I might go crazy waiting that long.

Suddenly my cellular rang. It was my wife, Maryam, calling to see how the test went. What would I tell her? How can I break the news to her? Is it something to really tell someone over the phone? She will know something is wrong by the tone of my voice, I am sure. I decided to let the call go to voicemail, and I drove home to tell her the news.

When I got home, Maryam instantly knew something was wrong by the look on my face. I told her with tears in my eyes. She sobbed, "Maybe it's a mistake... maybe they need to repeat the scan... maybe another radiologist needs to read it and see if they think the same."

"Maryam, it's not necessary. My radiologist is sure of what she saw."

We hugged. I explained the urologist was not overly concerned and we had a 3:00 pm appointment. My wife replied, "I'm going with you, no matter what."

It was three o'clock in the waiting room. It seemed like an eternity. "Dr. Conte?" came the call. We both followed the nurse into the exam room. I couldn't sit. I was pacing back and forth in this little room that was no bigger than eight by ten. My friend came in dressed in his white coat with two x-rays in his hands. He smiled, shook my hand, put the films up on the board and flipped on the light. As the lights flashed on, illuminating the x-rays, I immediately focused in on my left kidney. BOOM! There it was, the little wretched alien, the THING growing inside of me. I could see it as plain as day.

"Well, here it is," he pointed right to what I was looking at. "In fact, I think it is less than 2.5 centimeters. It measures more like 2 or 1.8 centimeters, which is even better."

"So what do I do now?" I asked.

"We take it out, do a partial nephrectomy[3], and leave the rest of the kidney behind." Easy for him to say. "When can you do it? Next Monday?" he asked.

That was five days away. What if it grew more, or worse – metastasized? "I have to wait five days? I want it out NOW!" He joked about just lying down and operating right here in his office. I wasn't in a joking mood. "OK, next week, Monday." I asked, "What time?"

"7:30 am at Baptist. See my O.R. coordinator and she will set everything up," he answered.

I needed to get the alien out of me as soon as possible. I began my preoperative journey which would include lab tests, an ECG[4], a CXR[5], and a letter from my cardiologist saying that my blood pressure was under control and it was okay to cut me.

August 5, 2005, could not come soon enough. I slept very little over the next four days, especially Sunday night. "Nothing to eat or drink after midnight" were the specific instructions. I was ready to go. "What if I don't wake up? Or, what if there is a problem and I bleed and need blood and end up in the ICU?" Again, a million thoughts raced in my mind. Finally the alarm went off at 5:30 am. I think I slept two hours total that night.

3 http://en.wikipedia.org/wiki/Nephrectomy
4 http://en.wikipedia.org/wiki/Ecg
5 http://www.enotes.com/surgery-encyclopedia/chest-x-ray

We both got dressed in silence avoiding the issue. My wife wanted to drive, so I took my packed bag and climbed into the passenger's seat. I kissed my children goodbye as they slept, and I wondered if I would ever see them again. They say that doctors make the worse patients, and I think that is true because we know what can happen and always think that it will happen to us.

We arrived at the hospital and got called into the pre-op area where I changed into my gown, had my IV started, and got some drugs for my severe anxiety. I waited for my surgeon. He finally arrived and as I was being wheeled out, I kissed my wife goodbye and whispered, "I love you." I saw her lips move, but in the noisy room, I was unable to make out what she said.

In the operating room, I was anesthetized without a problem. I woke up in what seemed to be five to ten minutes later. I was in the recovery room, without pain and wearing an oxygen mask. "I MADE IT!!!" I screamed inside my head.

I spent the next ten days in the hospital recovering, but finally went home, and that experience is a whole other story. Let's just say that it opened my eyes to what patients have to go through and changed my perspective on how I practice medicine.

Every six months, my CAT scans keep coming out negative, and my blood tests are stable. So for now it looks like we caught the alien in time and got it all out. Unfortunately, with every new pain or ache, I think the cancer has returned until finally that ache or pain goes away. It is no fun living like this, but many people do.

I was given a second chance, and I have tried to make the best of it. I appreciate the time with my wife and kids more. I appreciate my work and coworkers more. I just appreciate life in general more than before, or as I call it "BC" (Before Cancer). It is unfortunate that sometimes you need a wake up call like that to stop and smell the roses, but with me the lessons learned will not go wasted. I also have a completely new-found empathy for my patients. Who would have guessed that a slight nagging ache in my lower back would make me a better physician, a better father and husband, and a better human being. ☀

Dr. Conte is a Senior Physician with the Miami-Dade County Health Department working in the Department of Epidemiology, Division of Disease Control.

The Collector

By Mort Laitner

s I opened the door of my SUV, I glanced down at the ground and observed a worn penny. My spirits lifted. Had I found a valuable coin to add to my numismatic past? I observed Lincoln's presidential face, the year 1941 and the mint mark "D." Since its Denver creation, sixty-seven years ago, this coin had made it to Miami. I automatically flipped the coin over.

The copper cent was also known as a wheat penny from the design on its back.

As I flipped the coin, my mind flashed back to the Colonial Inn Motel (181 Street and Collins, Miami Beach). Who can forget the white marbled horses pulling a freshly painted black four-wheel buggy, complete with cement steps for the tourists to climb aboard. What a photo op! The year was 1959 and a ten-year-old coin collector studied the mound of change his father had deposited on the motel writing desk.

The boy found a 1909 VDB Lincoln penny in this mound. Over the next eight years, he collects Franklin halves, Morgan dollars, Indian head cents... Coin collecting was more than a hobby, it was a mild obsession and he treasured his coins as much as his first girlfriend, his '67 Mustang or his Head skis.

As I inserted the penny into my wallet for safekeeping, I noticed my Health Department business cards. I began to think about my career. Had I collected any treasures along the way?

First, interesting job titles: the swimming pool solicitor (environmental health), the raccoon attorney (rabies), the laser-beam lawyer (environmental safety), the birdman barrister (psittacosis – parrot fever), and the peepshow prosecutor (AIDS).

Where else but in a Health Department could have I collected these comical monikers? Then my mind wandered to my days of seeking fame and I realized I had a media collection: CBS National News, New York Times, St. Louis Dispatch, Life and Money magazines.

Where else could a minor league attorney get this national media coverage? As I scratched my head, I thought of the different hats I have worn with the agency: prosecuted cases and defended, drafted legislation and I've even worn the hat of a judge.

Where else but a Health Department? I've worn many other hats: building project manager, film director, producer and a bio-terrorism field exercise coordinator, party planner, author and lecturer. And now, I am writing and publishing.

Where else but in the Health Department could I have the freedom to venture out into so many fields? Next, I thought about my collection of interesting experiences:

- The experience of saving a newborn's life (obtaining a court-ordered blood transfusion);
- Being cursed by a gypsy in an adoption case (so far the curse hasn't taken hold, wait a minute... my weight gain... the patch);
- Having my life threatened by a young man, (whose water well we determined was contaminated.) He angrily had yelled over the phone, "I got a bullet in my gun with your name on it." Without fear, I calmly gave him a wrong address;
- The AIDS related case in the Key West, (where from the moment I got on the plane in Miami, people were talking about the case, and the general hum of gossip continued at the Key West Airport, during my Taxi ride to the hotel and my walk down Duval street on the way to the Courthouse). The whole town was abuzz with my case.

Where else but the Health Department? I've even collected a number of memorable character witnesses:

- Sir Lancelot Jones[1], a well-read gentle man who taught US presidents how to bone fish in the Keys;
- A soldier who dropped the A-bomb on Nagasaki;
- Rudolf Hess' US army doctor at Spandau prison;
- Evil Eye Finkle[2], who used his looks to intimidate boxers at ringside.

Where else but the Health Department could I meet these interesting individuals? At lunch, I opened my wallet to pay for my meal. The penny jumped out and hit the ground. Heads! As I picked up the coin, I observed the President's face, Abe smiled: "Son, You're lucky you chose a career in public health."

---

1 http://atlanta.creativeloafing.com/gyrobase/Content?oid=oid%3A11049
2 http://www.thesweetscience.com/boxing-article/2245/evil-eye-finkle-two-parts-voodoo-one-part-fraud

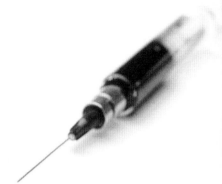

Injected with Fear

By Amy Tejirian

The warm, sunny February day in Los Angeles was the complete antithesis of where I was the day before. I could not believe how hot it was for a winter's day. That morning I had taken a one-way plane ride to LA from Calgary, Canada, the only home I had known in my eleven years. As the plane was taking off, my eyes gushed with tears. I did not want to move. I loved my hometown.

After my family and I had arrived at LAX, my parents immediately tried to enroll me at my new school. The school board informed us that my sister and I needed to get TB tests. My family trekked to the Glendale Health Center a couple blocks away from my new house. As we waited for our turn, I started to feel the fatigue setting in of moving to a new country that morning. Finally, they called my number. I sat down in front of the nurse, and my mom handed her my Canadian immunization record. The nurse glanced at my name then started to ask me questions in some language that was not English. I just stared at her blankly. Then in English she asked, "You are Armenian right?" I nodded. She continued, "You don't speak the language?" I said I did but had no idea that she was speaking Armenian to me. This was a culture shock. In Calgary, when people asked what nationality I was, I responded Armenian. They would usually look confused and say, "Oh Romanian?" And in Calgary, when I spoke Armenian with my family, it was like our own secret language that no one else could understand. Here in Glendale, most of the city's residents as well as the nursing staff at this Health Department were Armenian, but I could not understand a single word this nurse was saying to me. The nurse decided to speak English. Later, I found out that she was speaking another dialect of Armenian.

The nurse then looked at my immunization record and declared, "Canadians don't know anything about immunizations!" This really offended me. I had just gotten the Rubella vaccine two days earlier in Calgary so that I would be compliant with all of my vaccines. The nurse pulled out a series of needles. She started preparing to give me shots in the arm. I did not understand what she was doing to me. She stabbed me in the arm with one needle, the tetanus shot. She pricked me again with another shot. And finally, she administered the TB injection. It all happened too quickly. I stood up and walked over to my mother to wait for my sister's turn. My sister sat in the same torture chair I had just sat in. All of a sudden I felt woozy. I opened my mouth to explain this to my mother, but as soon as I did, my head started to spin. The next thing I can remember was waking up, lying on an exam table with my feet in the air. The odor of pungent smelling salts irritated my nose. "What happened?" It turns out that I had a little seizure and I fainted. Welcome to America. For the next couple days my arm was incredibly sore from the tetanus shot. I could barely lift it up. After the TB test results came in negative I was allowed to attend school.

Fast forward sixteen years to when I was due to receive another tetanus shot, I avoided it like the plague. I knew it was important to get but my past experience left a bitter taste in my mouth. I could not avoid the tetanus shot forever.

In 2006, the Miami-Dade County Health Department was conducting their employee immunization drive. I wanted to get my flu shot so I had obtained my old immunization record from my high school. I waited as colleague after colleague received vaccines and flu shots. Then it was my turn. I sat in the dreaded chair and handed over my records. It was clear that I was long overdue for my tetanus shot. I was a nervous wreck. The fear ran rampant through my rigid body. Everyone from SIP (Special Immunization Project) was trying to calm me. Tracie, my co-worker, tried to distract me as my arm was getting prepped for the shots. To my surprise, in a couple of minutes it was all over. I didn't feel sick at all. Further, my arm was not sore afterwards.

First Lady Eleanor Roosevelt said it best, "You gain strength, courage and confidence by every experience in which you really stop to look fear in the face. You must do the thing you think you cannot do." That hot, humid Miami afternoon, I looked fear in the face and gained self-confidence. ☼

My Habit

By Morton Laitner

Getting Started...

As a 13 year-old growing up in the Catskill Mountains, I can remember smoking my first cigarette as if it were yesterday. Joel, Bobby, Donna, Rissa and I had concocted a plan to smoke our first cigarette. My friends and I thought it was cool to smoke. When do you get a chance to share hits with a pretty girl? We snuck into a rock formation called "Dead Man's Canyon" to smoke our parents' pilfered Newports, Marlboros, and Camels. The canyon consisted of two thirteen-foot-high by ten-foot-wide, thirty-thousand-pound boulders situated approximately eight feet apart. These boulders had been moved in place during the last great ice-age. Legend has it that either some Iroquois Indians carrying tomahawks and bows and arrows or a large brown bear was chasing a fur capped frontiersman who attempted to escape by leaping across the eight-foot gap. Slipping, he fell into the crevasse, hit his head, and broke his neck. Needless to say he died.

Dead Man's Canyon was the perfect place to hide and smoke a few cigarettes. Parents or police would hardly ever venture into this part of the wilderness. The first time we went there and every time after, we felt like adults as we inhaled the white menthol-flavored smoke. Even these filtered cigarettes caused us to cough as we felt the burning smoke enter our lungs.

Tobacco was our forbidden fruit. In those days my parents smoked up to two packs a day. As a teenager, I distinctly remember my father, who was a medical doctor, waking up in the morning and going to the bathroom in his boxers to hack-up his lungs. The tobacco companies never offered my dad royalties for a TV commercial showing the phlegm dripping out of his mouth. You would think this memory alone would have taught me to not smoke. However, we were continually bombarded with advertisements of beautiful young models sitting next to flowing streams with the look of love in their eyes as they lit up. My other favorite was the ultra-macho Marlboro Cowboys riding stallions in red stone canyons and then resting with a Marlboro hanging off their lips. How could we simple teenagers not want to be these lucky people? And it was cheap. A pack cost as little as thirty-five cents; vices were so much cheaper in the good ole' days.

These were the days:
- A twelve year old could go into the corner grocery and buy a pack, no questions asked.
- Cigarettes were rarely called cancer sticks or nails in one's coffin.
- No one had even thought of the Great American Smokeout.
- The tobacco companies did not want us to know that smoking was the cause of approximately 80% of lung cancer deaths.
- The surgeon general was not warning us that, "Cigarette smoking may injure your health."
- Tobacco companies lied to us; never thinking they would get caught.
- Every media outlet made millions of dollars advertising cigarettes. Who could blame them for not telling the truth?
- Doctors in advertisements would recommend a particular brand of cigarettes.
- On a flight to Miami on Eastern Airlines, every passenger would get a cute-looking-mini- five-pack as a gratuity and of course for the industry to hook the unsuspecting with their poison. Hard to believe that people used to smoke on airplanes.
- Pregnant women were not warned of the dangers of smoking.

Getting hooked...
My habit through high school and college was limited to a few cig-

arettes a week. However by law school, with the pressure on, a half a pack-a-day was not unusual. By the time I was a lawyer with the Department of Health and Rehabilitative Services my office was filled with smoke to the point that my non-smoking secretary would cough every time she took dictation. Today, I feel guilty for my thoughtless behavior. I did not know the dangers of second-hand smoke.

By the early eighties, my boss, Dr. Richard Morgan, Director of the Miami-Dade County Health Department, was a key player in the Dade County Medical Association Anti-Tobacco drive. Doctors campaigned against smoking in the work place, smoking in health facilities, and the advertisement of tobacco products.

These were the days when:

My dad had an 8 inch Goodyear rubber tire ashtray on his medical office desk which almost always was stuffed with Camel butts.

Kick-Your-Habit nicotine chewing gum and sucking candy did not exist.

Many smokers collected Zippo lighters. My most treasured was the one with Joe Camel riding a motor cycle through New York City near the World Trade Center.

I also collected sterling-silver-cigarette cases and when I removed a cigarette from the shiny case I felt like a Hollywood silent film star in the nineteen twenties.

My next door neighbor, who was so addicted to the toxic weed, smoked even after he was diagnosed with emphysema. He would remove his oxygen mask light up even to the day he died.

Kicking the Habit....

One of the hardest things to do in my life was kicking my twenty year habit. One a.m. would find me in my closet with my hands in my sports-coat pockets scrounging for a cigarette to feed my habit.

I bummed cigarettes in the hopes of smoking less than a pack a day. My smoking friends now thought I was a pain in the butt. Quitting was made more difficult because my wife – with a one cigarette a day habit – always kept a pack in the house.

I tried the reward system in which for every day that I did not smoke, I would add a few dollars to the kitty to purchase a desired gift. However my daily one-hour drive home still required five cigarettes. Even with these gimmicks, I woke up coughing my lungs out – just like my dad – at this moment, I knew I had to quit.

I can't remember my last cigarette, I know I sucked on nicorette candy and chewed nicorette gum for over two weeks. I knew that just like an alcoholic, I had to resolve that my lips, my tongue, my lungs would never again taste tobacco because if they did I would be hooked all over again.

I haven't smoked a cigarette in over 20 years.

As I now stand in Dead Man's Canyon remembering my boyhood, my parents, and my friends as I look at the chasm between the two large boulders, I realize when I smoked I was careening between the rocks. Luckily, I grabbed on to the ledge pulling myself onto the large stone when I kicked my deadly habit. However, my habit was not as lucky – it died like the frontiersman.

On the Wings of Angels

By Paula Mooty
Original Artwork by Vicki F. MootyJones

A s I sat in the cemetery on a cool October evening, inhaling the sweet fragrance of jasmine, my eyes squinted as the golden evening sun touched the outstretched wings of cemetery angels. Suddenly, I spied two familiar names on a tombstone. The names were Victoria and Thomas Taylor. This reminded me of a story told by my Grandmother, Eliza Downing.

Around the late 1800's, the Taylors and the Downings started families in the small town of Fernandina which lies across the river from Jacksonville. At that time, Florida was only a state of sand, sea, and swamps. One weekend in June 1888, the Taylors and Downings gathered to discuss the qualities of summers in Florida: the heat, humidity, rain, disease and the inevitable hurricanes. They spoke about yellow fever, malaria, cholera, smallpox, dengue fever and consumption (tuberculosis). The ominous conversations were sweetened with fresh, cool lemonade but the sour taste of fear lay heavy as they rested their heads on their pillows that night. In the depth of the evening, my great aunt Maggie Downing, a young teen, awoke with a fever, sweats, nausea and a headache. She wondered if she had food poisoning. By morning, she was dehydrated and weak from lack of sleep. Her parents rushed her to the family doctor. Maggie had been sick before but never like this.

After hitching up the carriage, crossing the river by ferry, and traveling for two hours, the family reached Jacksonville. They hurried to Dr. Brown's office. Dr. Brown diagnosed yellow fever. They knew the effect this news would have on Maggie, not to mention the community. Under a blanket of secrecy, Dr. Brown transferred Maggie to Jacksonville's St. Luke's Hospital.

As Maggie's temperature rose, her skin turned a yellow-green color. Maggie experienced intestinal bleeding and vomiting. In her delirium, she hallucinated eating with her brothers and sister on the veranda of their big house. Maggie's siblings were breakfasting on fresh blueberries, milk, and buttered biscuits covered with homemade strawberry jam. She imagined that she was going to the wharf to watch the schooners set sail. She envisioned the cool sea breezes and tasted the salty air while beads of sweat ran down her face. In her hospital bed, Maggie lay fighting the Angel of Death.

She won. Maggie was fortunate; she was well enough to go home after a month in the hospital. Before her release, four more cases were secretly admitted to St. Luke's. This was the beginning of the epidemic. Jacksonville business leaders feared if the epidemic news leaked, the city would go bankrupt. They decided this news had to be kept from the public. They would have to contain this disease. Dr. Brown contacted Dr. Andrew Downing, Maggie's brother, to be his assistant. As Dr. Andrew learned of the details of the disease, he knew that he must be part of the solution to help those in the same predicament as his sister.

Dr. Joseph Yates Porter, a medical officer with the U.S. Marine Hospital Service, was contacted to help curtail the outbreak. He was known for his work with the yellow fever epidemics in Key West. Dr. Porter had success in arresting the spread of the disease the previous year because his experience had led him to believe that the sick needed to be isolated from one another. Dr. Porter noticed that recovered patients were able to work with ill patients without being reinfected. He applied this strategy in fighting this grave disease.

If quarantine were to be declared in Jacksonville, there would be no safe haven for those fleeing the city to take refuge. Doctors Downing, Brown and Porter contacted the U.S. Public Health Service and the Red Cross for aid. Relief came in the guise of $200,000 from the U.S. Government and arrival of the Red Cross. Dr. Porter requested that a registered nurse, Jane Delano, be summoned to assist during the epidemic. She worked in the hospital organizing treatment of patients.

Dr. Downing flipped through ten years of ledger of Fernandina residences. He glanced at his silver pocket watch and noticed he had been searching for three hours. He found thirty-five survivors of the 1877 epidemic. Would they be willing to help care for the current yellow fever victims? Twenty-five survivors accepted the call of duty. Late in the afternoon, the brave twenty-five gathered outside Fernandina's public school for their departure. After a blessing by the Methodist minister, they set out for Jacksonville on horseback, ox cart and carriage.

The Jacksonville inhabitants panicked when the news of Yellow Fever "leaked." Even though the city's 26,000 citizens were already under quarantine, a mass exodus commenced. People fled in the dark of night on foot, horseback, steamer, train, boat, carriage, or ox cart to get away from the "Yellow Jack." Deputies on horseback carrying yellow flags (the quarantine flag) and sharp-shooter rifles were positioned to prevent the populace from entering or leaving without a special pass. Gunfire echoed as refugees crossed the temporary boundaries.

The city was under marshal law from dusk to dawn; a curfew was signaled by the loud boom of a cannon. Food became scarce; stores and hotels closed; social events and mail ceased. Mail was fumigated and lime was spread on the streets in an effort to contain the disease's spread. Bonfire flames lit the evening sky fueled by clothing and bedding.

Many residents escaped, some were shot and others turned back when confronted. Thousands became sick and hundreds died. When would this nightmare end? Jacksonville was a city under siege.

As the chill of the November morning settled on the Downing

house, Maggie, home for a few months and still weak from her bout with Yellow Jack, finished setting the table when Papa Downing and Doc Andrew walked through the front door. Wearily, they entered the dining room and with a great sigh of relief made the long anticipated announcement, "No new cases have been reported for more than ten days. It looks like the epidemic is over."

Mother and Hattie, the housekeeper, ran into the room when they heard the news. Mother cried and hugged Papa. As they sat around the table, they thanked God for the deliverance from the yellow fever epidemic. The epidemic of 1888 finally came to an end after the first winter freeze that eliminated the mosquito population. The final count was 5,000 cases and 500 dead. [1]

As darkness blanketed the cemetery, I pictured an angel carrying brave men like Doc Reed and Doc Porter on its outstretched wings. I realized that public health servants are doing the work of angels on earth. ☼

1 On August 27, 1900, an Army physician, James Carroll, allowed an infected mosquito to feed on him. He developed a severe case of yellow fever which allowed his colleague, Dr. Walter Reed, to prove the dreaded disease was transmitted by mosquitoes. Yellow fever was the first human virus to be isolated and classified as a virus. Dr. Porter became Florida's first State Health Officer in 1888. The State Board of Health of Florida was established in 1889. The vector of yellow fever, Aedes aegypti, was discovered in 1900 by U.S. Army physicians. In 1927, the causative agent of yellow fever, Flaviavirus, was isolated and identified by Dr. Walter Reed. This discovery led to the development of a vaccine in 1937. Jane Delano, R.N., a distant relative of Franklin Delano Roosevelt, was a volunteer for the Army Reserve Corps ("ARC") and established the Nursing Corp for the American Red Cross in 1909-1912; The Nursing Corp enabled the United States to enter the First World War with a ready team of nurses numbering eight-thousand.

'Cause These Are The Good Old Days

By Morton Latiner

While driving my SUV with the radio blaring, Carly Simon's syrupy voice pouring out the words to the song, "Anticipation", her 1971 classic, while I sing along.

> *Anticipation, anticipation is making me late,*
> *is keeping me waiting.*
> *We can never know about the days to come.*
> *But we think about them any way.*

Together, Carly and I vocalized: *'cause these are the good old days.*

I glanced over at Tracie, who to my surprise was lip-synching, and remarked, "Wow, what a great song. Too bad most of your generation has never heard it. They never even saw the Heinz 57 commercial which used the tune. Kids could learn an important life lesson if they listened."

Tracie laughed while thinking about one of their recent Health

Department projects, "Mort, if you had written that song the title would have been: "Procrastination.""

Mort chuckled as he retorted, "Some people sure know how to procrastinate and I am one of the best!" He continued, "You know, throughout my health department career, I've heard:

Get immunized;

Wash you hands;

Eat right, exercise;

Get your annual physical;

Test your cholesterol;

Don't Smoke;

Be prepared;

Wear protection;

Don't procrastinate...

"So you would think that these public health messages would sink into my thick skull. But, as most of our nurses are aware, health messages alone get little response until the matter at hand becomes urgent. Tracie, remember my fear of the surgeon's silvery scalpel!" Mort exclaimed as he licked his teeth with his tongue.

Tracie shook her head in the negative, and asked, "What happened?"

Mort shuttered as he remembered his most lengthy and unhealthy procrastination.... a story spanning two decades.

Mort began, "One morning back in '87, I observed two protrusions on my body. Wondering what the protrusions were, and with the fear of the unknown outweighing my desire to wait, I promptly made an appointment with my family doctor.

He advised that I had two hernias.

"Doc, what should I do?" The kind-hearted physician replied, "Son, at this stage I would say wait until you are in pain and then have surgery to repair them."

Over the next twenty years, when I was on shopping adventures with my wife in the Sawgrass, Broward or Pembroke Pines mall, I would get a burning sensation in this region of my body. And it was not from my credit cards!

My remedy was simple; I would sit in a chair for approximately 15 minutes. Then the discomfort would subside and I could continue proclaiming that my wife's newest acquisitions were exactly what we needed at the house.

I had successfully avoided my hernia surgery for twenty years.

Then one fateful Hurricanes-versus-Tarheels Saturday afternoon, we walked two miles to get to and from the Orange Bowl. That night, I was lying in bed with sharp excruciating pains piercing through my left side.

I prayed to the God of procrastinators, "Please stop this pain! Please no surgery!"

Awakening often throughout the night, my prayers went unheeded.

That morning, in agony, I whimpered my story to the wife.

Now the process was out-of-control – doctors, nurses, an ambulance, and finally the hospital.

As I slipped out of consciousness, I kept thinking about the dreaded surgeon's sharp silvery scalpel slicing into my soft skin; my twenty years of procrastination had finally ended.

I somehow survived seven hellish days of hard recuperation - IVs, liquid diet, pain killers, shots, bandages and the passing of many hours in silent boredom.

Tracie hears me sing, "Recuperation, recuperation is making me hate, is keeping me waiting." She gives me her weak joke smile.

As we continue down I-95, Tracie realizes how happy my restored health had made me and I realize the joy of a new healthy beginning.

"Carly was right," Tracie acknowledges.

"We can never know about the days to come."

After a pregnant pause we both magically and simultaneously blurt out: *"Cause these are the good old days."* ☼

Scars

By Mort Laitner

Sitting in the Senior Leadership meeting, I glanced down at my hands, observing the scars that I wear. The crescent moon-shaped scar between my thumb and index finger was caused by experimenting with gun powder, removed from sparklers, then inserted into glass tubing. The resulting explosion ended my rocket-engine testing career. I remember my dad treating my wounds as I shook with fear of mercurochrome, verbal punishment and seeing blood pouring out of my hands. I didn't have to worry about the verbal punishment because of the deafening ringing in my ears. My dad, a family doctor, acted professionally. I sensed he expected this less-than-bright activity from his only son. My dad did not lack emotional intelligence.

My eyes moved to the tip of my right hand ring finger. I remembered my recent knife fight with a two day old poppy seed bagel. I lost.

My mind left my hands and moved to the rest of my body. I pictured my twelve-stitch appendectomy scar. I was twelve years old;

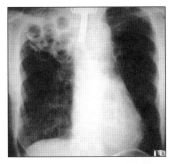

Multiple round ring-shadows in RUL are plastic balls inserted into the pleural space to collapse lung

my concerned parents entered my post-op hospital room. I moaned in agony from the effects of ether. I begged them for ice as my parched throat cries. Then my parents drop a bomb. "Son, the surgeon said your surgery was unnecessary. Your appendix was normal. It was some glands around the appendix which were causing your pain." Their words scarred my heart. I yell out my request, "Get the hell out of the room!"

Those words were costly. A year later, G-d punished me for breaking one of his commandments with the teenage plague, acne, and its resultant scars.

But now my brain focused on the most intriguing scar story of my life. This time the scar was on someone else's body.

Twenty years ago, I was researching cases on the subject of tuberculosis in the law library.

I had befriended the elderly librarian. We often talked of the cases I was handling. I mentioned that I was going to court to have a person with tuberculosis committed to A.G. Holly Hospital. Irving, a mild-mannered man in his sixties, matter-of-factly said to me, "Well, since we are talking about TB, I have something to show you." I watched him remove his bow-tie, his highly starched white shirt and, to my amazement, his undershirt. He then turned his back to me. I observed two large scars under each side of his rib cage. Irving explained, "When I was a child in the early 1940's, I contracted TB. To keep me breathing, the doctors placed many ping pong balls into my lungs. Those ping pong balls kept me alive. They gave me an additional fifty years." Irving proudly wore his scars.

As my mind returned to the Senior Leadership meeting, I realized that wound repair is a natural part of the healing process. Having observed Irving's scars, I wondered how many times I had been stabbed in the back. As an attorney for over thirty years, I knew these worn wounds serve as countless reminders of battles fought and proudly survived. ❀

Immortality

By Morton Laitner

As a bookish thirteen-year-old lad, I read the World Book En-cyclopedia from A to Z. It was 1965 and I lived in New York's Catskill Mountains. On cold wintery days, nothing gave me more pleasure than learning about the outside world through the pages of my World Book. In volume "M", I studied mortality and wondered how to not to attain it.

Forty-five years later (2005), with the advent of Wikipedia, my old reading habit resurfaced. Now on a daily basis, I scan a few pages of this computer generated encyclopedia. On one of those pages, I learned about the London Lock Hospital[1] which was the first venereal disease clinic in the world. The clinic was opened in 1747 and treated nearly three hundred patients in its first year. The demand for its services stemmed from the unfounded belief that the treatments then available could be effective. As I continued to read, I learned that the memory of the hospital continued with the annual award of the London Lock Hospital Memorial Prize in Sexually Transmitted Diseases at the Royal Free Hospital School of Medicine.

London Lock Hospital's two hundred years of name-recognition-

1 http://en.wikipedia.org/wiki/London_Lock_Hospital

immortality triggered a memory. Ironically, also one founded in the field of sexually transmitted diseases.

Here is my immortality story.

The air in my 1986 Ford Aero star minivan was a comfortable 70 degrees. We were cruising on U.S. 27 headed north to Graceland. The family was on its annual summer pilgrimage. My three boys started to read out loud these homemade billboard signs attached to tall naked cypress trees. Jason shouts, "Ten miles to Tom Gaskins Cypress Knee Museum. Dad, lets go there!" It must have been 98 degrees in the shade and with the hot thick syrupy air this diversion would be loads of fun. I'll play the silent father and see how badly the kids want to go. Travis is next, he reads, "Only eight miles to see the lady hippo wearing the Carmen Miranda's hat. Dad, how can we by-pass that!" I sarcastically said, "You have a point". Finally Blake clinched the deal. "Pop, the sign says, swamp catwalk and gift shop." I thought out loud, "What can you buy in a cypress knee museum gift shop?"

We strolled above the swamp on the catwalk as mosquitoes feasted on our bodies. In the museum, we observed cypress knees[2] in the shape of Flipper, Josef Stalin's face and who could ever forget the lady hippo wearing the fruit-laden Carmen Miranda hat. But now the coup de grace – the gift shop. It was loaded with cypress knees of every conceivable shape and size.

And then I saw it!

The knee was an icon for the aids program. I knew my friend, David, who ran the Health Department AIDS program would highly appreciate it. Would Dave have the nerve to house it in his office? These were the days when state senators opposed AIDS posters showing condoms. I told my wife, "Now I know what people buy in a cypress knee museum gift shops." Tom Gaskins, owner and museum proprietor, personally bubble wrapped my gift to insure its safety. I humbly advised Mr. Gaskins that the knee would be used as an AIDS educational tool. Tom looked me in the eyes and in his best

2 Cypress Knees are protuberances – usually roughly conical in shape and from one to nine feet in length.

Florida drawl said, "Izzahsoo, Now I've heard it all!"

On my return to the Health Department, I presented Dave with the cypress knee. Dave adored the gift. Here are his exact words, "Mort, you will never know how much this gift means to me." He loved it so much that at the next Statewide AIDS conference he awarded the knee to the county health AIDS unit that had the best yearly surveillance results.

And so year-after-year the tradition continued. The knee award travelled throughout the state.

Then one day in the beginning of the new century, I was giving a lecture to members of the Florida Public Health Association. A young FPHA member who was in the audience approached me and said, "I'm really glad to meet the person whose name is attached to the AIDS Surveillance Award." In total astonishment, I replied, "Thanks for the info. I did not know the cypress knee became an award nor that it was named after me.

As I left the hotel ballroom, I wondered if I would ever again see the award which carries my name and laughed in the face of my mortality. ☼

Editor's Note:
During hard times, one of the first things people loose is their sense of humor. Remember laughter is the best medicine.

3 Cypress knees, the part of the cypress tree's root system not submerged below water, come in a variety of evocative shapes and sizes. The greatest knee poacher of all time was a man named Tom Gaskins, proprietor of the Cypress Knee Museum in Palmdale, Florida. He collected hundreds of knees from 23 states, and held the only US patent on cypress knee manufacture. His collection included one knee that resembled Joseph Stalin and another described as a "lady hippo wearing a Carmen Miranda hat." Cutting off knees kills the cypress tree, so today, thanks to the Lady Bird Johnson Law, knee poaching is illegal. Gaskins' collection was destined to be the last of its kind. Unfortunately, following Gaskins' death in 1998 and a major burglary in 2000, the museum closed. http://www.kirchersociety.org/blog/2007/07/18/tom-gaskins-cypress-knee-museum/

The Handshake
El Darse las Manos

By Morton Laitner

I t's funny how some memories stick with you. Here's one of mine. It was a hot sweaty, pre-Al Gore global warming Miami day, as my hands tightly held on to the steering wheel of my fire-engine red 260Z Datsun (Nissan). My hands were as slippery as a mackerel lying on a Publix fish counter. I was listening to the oldies station, Magic, 102.7 on the FM dial.

The DJ was playing the classic 1964 Beatles tune, "I Want To Hold Your Hand".

Pause – thought – "How would that translate in Español?" "Quiero Agarrar Tu Mano". I think that's correct. The tune is catchy and I sang it out loud, over and over again in my off-tune bellowing voice. This sweltering heat and humidity wasn't going to affect this teenage memory.

Keep driving as the sun's rays were glaring off of my Foster Grants.

Pause – thought – "What did I know about communicable diseases when I was fifteen years old, and living in the Catskill Mountains in 1964."

Mumps (paperas) had it, painful golf-ball size salivary gland below my upper jaw one summer week on the right side of my face and exactly seven days later same protrusion on my left.

Measles (sarampión) had it. Doctor said, "Don't scratch!" But of course listening was and is not one of my strong points and some itches just have got be scratched.

Pause – silence, deep in thought – and yes there was that young neighborhood boy who always walked with his wooden crutch. What was his name? He had polio (poliomelitis). Quick visual pictures crossed my mind: FDR, iron lung, Salk, Sabin, needles, oral spray, vaccines, the miracles of science.

I was driving to give a lecture on this newly-named communicable disease, AIDS (Síndrome de Inmuno-Deficiencia Adquirida). I would talk about protecting confidentiality and discrimination of persons with AIDS (PWA).

Entering the lecture hall at the University of Miami, I was introduced to Pedro the co-lecturer. Pedro would talk about the disease that was now becoming hottest news story. AIDS paranoia was spreading like wild fire. How was it spread? Sex, needles, eating utensils, razors? How do you get this deadly disease?

I had not met anybody with AIDS that I knew of.

We shook hands and I sat down to listen to Pedro teach. As he spoke I observed white fungus looking pustules (oral candidiasis or thrush) on his tongue and palate. He had AIDS – pause – in my head the room fell silent.

Life-threatening paranoia filled my brain.
WE HAD SHOOK HANDS. OH MY GOD!
NOS HEMOS DADO LAS MANOS. HAY DIOS MIO!

My hands and forehead started to sweat profusely.

As my speech ended, I politely said good-bye to Pedro and to the UM hosts. Not offering my hand to anyone. I exited the hall urgently looking for a bathroom. Entering the men's room I proceeded to pump a vast quantity of liquid soap in to my hands and rubbing them together as hard as possible. I have never scrubbed my hands so hard. I must get those viruses down the sink!

Today, as I am driving my navy blue Honda CRV listening to

Beatles singing, "I Want To Hold Your Hand" this memory seems laughable but at the time it was frightening. Pause – thought – so what did I learn. Fear will cause some memories to stick with you for a lifetime.

It has been years since I thought about the handshake and my fear of the unknown. This memory has stuck with me for over twenty-three years. And, it is quite embarrassing to tell this story but it merits telling. ☀

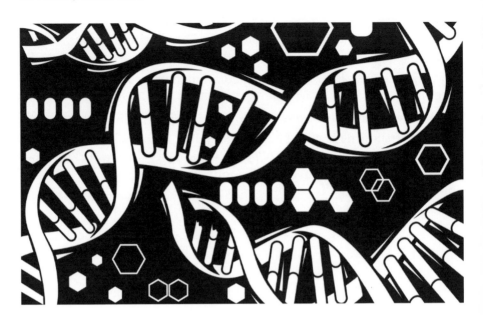

Kindness of Strangers

By Tracie Dickerson

"Miss, can I call you a taxi?" said the male nurse.

I slowly become aware of my surroundings. My vision was blurred. I'm in a small room at a Texas blood bank. I am sitting in a chair signing forms I cannot read. My eyes are puffy and red. I am scared and I am alone.

"Miss?" He said again.

"No. I just need a minute." I tearfully replied. My mind was elsewhere. I was lost and had stopped listening again. I am eighteen. I am a freshman in college. And I am going to die.

"Please sign this form. Your social security number will be placed on a list of people with HIV. You can no longer donate blood."

I don't remember much about the days that followed that conversation. But I do remember the next thing I did was go for a second medical opinion. The painful prick of the needle was the last thing on my mind as my doctor took a few vials of blood. I watched as he drew the warm liquid into the test tubes and wondered how much longer I would get to live. In my dark and confused state, I heard my doctor say, "I will give you a call in seven days."

During the next seven days I contemplated my 18 years of existence. I lost my taste for food and my sense of smell vanished. I hoped that the first HIV positive result was wrong. I did not want to scare my family. I couldn't tell anyone or confide in my friends. My college had less than one thousand students. If this got out, I would never be able to show my face again. I felt like a leper. I stopped attending classes. If I was going to die, what difference would a diploma make? In my naiveté, I thought I could transmit HIV to the toddlers and two year olds that I was taking care of, so I called in sick from my job as a teacher at the church day care.

In my hellish self-imposed exile, I spent hours wondering how I could have gotten infected. Then I wondered how long I would have left to live. In my state of denial I refused to go on the internet to learn about any anti-virals, like AZT, that might help me live longer.

I had just gotten out of the shower when the call came. I shivered when I heard my doctor's voice on the other end of the line. My test results were in. I steeled myself for the news. I stood there, dripping water onto the cold tile floor. After an excruciatingly long pause, my doctor said, "Tracie, I am going to have to ask you to come to the clinic for a consultation. I am not allowed to give your test results via telephone." I put my hand on the nightstand as I made my way to my bed. I did not want to pass out on the dirty dorm floor.

I trembled as I returned the receiver to the cradle. I was terrified. If it was good news, why wouldn't he just tell me? I am going to die. I needed a friend but didn't know who to trust. I heard a knock at my door. I opened it, and there stood Bill, a friend of my roommate and a virtual stranger to me. He could tell something was wrong.

Bill asked, "Tracie, you look pale as a ghost, are you okay? Can I help you?" I confided in him. He drove me to the doctor's office. We waited together for the test results. This kind stranger calmed me. I thought of Tennessee William's play, A Streetcar Named Desire, and Blanche Dubois' line, "I've always depended on the kindness of strangers." For the first time in my life, I understood what she meant.

It felt like a lifetime passed before I met with my doctor. My body felt heavy as I prepared for the bad news. I was comforted to know that Bill would drive me back home once my death sentence was pronounced. My doctor cleared his throat, "Your results are negative." He smiled and gave me the first hug I had in over a week.

An enormous weight floated off of my shoulders. My first HIV test had been a false positive.

Although we never spoke again, I often think of Bill as one of my personal heroes and I still don't even know his last name. But he was there when I needed someone.

Sometimes during crisis we are sent a kind stranger to help us shoulder our burdens. ☀

The Three Mitzvahs[1]

By Tracie Dickerson and Mort Laitner

As Tracie trudged up the steps of the old Flagler Street Courthouse, she glanced up at the strangely shaped nimbus clouds blanketing the dark sky. She thought, "It's going to be one hell-of-a-bad day." Today, Tracie's job required her to evict a poor family from their ramshackle trailer. Entering the Judge's chambers, Tracie heard soft background music coming from Bose speakers. Tracie thought, "I know that Paul Simon song." She hummed along.

"No, I would not give you false hope,
On this strange and mournful day,
But the mother and child reunion,
Is only a motion away, o little 'darling' of mine."[2]

---

1 http://en.wikipedia.org/wiki/Mitzvah
2 "Mother and Child Reunion" is a song written by Paul Simon, the name has its origin in a chicken and egg dish called "Mother and Child Reunion" that Paul Simon saw on a Chinese restaurant's menu. The song has been interpreted as a meditation on death, specifically the death of a mother and the hope of reunification in the afterlife. http://en.wikipedia.org/wiki/Mother_and_child_reunion

Tracie was representing the Health Department in a sanitary nuisance[3] case. The case involved a mother and son who were dumping raw sewage onto their property. Kitty, a sixty-something mother, and her thirty-something son were also taking this untreated sewage in buckets in the back of a pick-up truck to the toilet at the local gas station.

Kitty hadn't always lived this way. She was married to a nice guy and lived in a nice house with her husband's children from another marriage. When her spouse passed away, the Court determined she had the right to live in the house until she died because her husband's will had left the house to his children.

It was a small Homestead house on a valuable piece of real estate... until Katrina and Wilma ravished it. The neighbors had stood idly by while Kitty, not having been accustomed to taking care of the family finances, obtained mortgages on the property. Her son, meanwhile, had turned the dilapidated house into a crack den. The police arrested Kitty's son. Then the County condemned and demolished the house. The son went off to jail. Kitty moved into a homeless shelter. A month later, with the help of her church, a trailer was donated and placed on her property. This 5' x 15' foot trailer had no electricity, no water and no sewer hook-ups, only a holding tank. When her son was released from jail, the neighbors started to complain to the Health Department.

On this dreary day, the issue before the court was whether or not mother and son should be evicted because the untreated sewage was leaking onto the ground. The neighbors saw and got a whiff of this nasty, noisome mess. These wealthy folks were up-in-arms about getting this smelly eye-sore out of their neighborhood.

Environmental Health Inspectors cited the mobile home as a health threat. They photographed an 8' x 5' foot fecal-sand pit and rodent-infested boxes of trash. Tracie sighed as she remembered her first trip to the property. When Kitty's house had been knocked down, all of her treasures were put in cardboard boxes and placed in the back corner of the yard. Tracie thought about all of the things she had collected in a lifetime and was moved when she wondered how difficult it would be for her memories to be destroyed by weather or rodents.

Now the parties met inside the judge's chambers to get the issue resolved. Tracie would soon learn that the lawyer had taken $250.00 out of his own pocket to have the trailer's holding tank pumped and

3 http://www.flsenate.gov/Statutes/index.cfm?App_mode=Display_Statute&URL=Ch0386/ch0386.htm

Kitty's son had removed the trash from the property, thereby abating the nuisance. Kitty testified, "Judge, if my son and I are moved into a homeless shelter, his mental health will collapse, and he will end up in jail again." Kitty drawled, "Darlin', please don't separate a mama from her baby. I beg ya, your Honna." The Judge smiled having never before been called "Darlin" in Court. The Judge then motioned, "I'll grant the injunction but allow this mother and son reunion to continue as long as no more sewerage hits the ground and that pit is covered. Kitty's eyes teared-up as she thanked the Judge. Her words wept, "God bless ya."

Tracie knew that Kitty was broke, relying upon the kindness of others for even the simplest necessities of life. As she walked down the courthouse steps, Tracie decided to travel the extra mile. She went to Home Depot to buy twenty pounds of lye[4] and an additional twenty pounds of sand. She then delivered and shoveled the sand and lye around the pit.

As Tracie looked down, her shoes covered in lye dust and her sandy hands still on the shovel, she felt a sun beam cutting through the clouds. Tracie smiled – three mitzvahs on one day: an attorney giving charity to his client, a judge giving compassion to a mother and son, and a government lawyer digging into her own pocket to help the family to stay together.

Tracie thought, "Not a bad ending for what started as a sad and dreary day."

http://en.wikipedia.org/wiki/Lye

TB or not TB: that is the Question?
(Apologies to W. Shakespeare)

By Morton Laitner

It was a rare cold clear steel blue February day in Miami. The type of windy day that Western-State sanatoriums loved to sit their tubercular patients on rocking chairs over looking the Rocky Mountains.

Outside of Ward D, a small group of individuals huddled together wearing their winter coats and sweaters. Ward D is a holding center at Jackson Memorial Hospital where noncompliant TB patients are jailed until a judge decides whether they will be quarantined at A.G Holley TB Hospital, located in Lantana, Florida.

They consisted of the Health Department physician, a TB investigator, a judge, a court reporter and an attorney appointed to represent JH[1] the alleged noncompliant tubercular suspect. Finally the Department's lawyer, Mort, who was forty pounds lighter than today, wore thick coke-bottle lenses, had a pack-a-day cigarette habit and didn't wear his signature suspenders and eye-patch.

---

1 Confidentiality laws require that we substitute a pseudonym for the true name of the patient and due process laws require counsel be appointed for people that might lose their freedom

Holding their drivers' licenses high above their heads, the group faced a sullen-looking correctional officer who sat behind a large glass window. The group now proceeded into the Sally port[2]. Each member donned two N-95 surgical masks. The second face mask was placed directly on top of the other. With much trepidation, the group slowly entered patient JH's windowless negative air-pressure chamber. The ten-by-ten cell contained a pure shiny metal toilet missing the normal plastic seat cover and an institutional white steel metal rack bed with five-inch thick stained mattress. Resting on the mattress was JH, wearing his two N-95 masks. He was a thirty-two year old gaunt male with pale white skin and a smattering of freckles.

JH had a predilection for cheap booze and any drug he could get his hands on. Of course, these nasty habits helped land JH in this sobering predicament.

The purpose of today's trial was for the Judge to determine the next 180 days of JH's life. The Judge would now have to decide, in part, did JH have contagious TB or not? JH would spend the next six months housed in the country's last freestanding TB sanatorium.

Now the trial combatants, participants, and one frightened TB patient squeezed into this small already well-heated room. The weight of their sweaters was overwhelming. The double masks stuck tight to their faces, their breaths audible as they unconsciously drew in the purified air. The heat in the room built as the trial started. Each person internally reflected on the dangers of taking off their life-saving masks for a drink of water to cool themselves. The condensation began to form on Mort's glasses. Now Mort had to do his cross-examination while wiping the fog that formed on his lenses. The court reporter swore in the witnesses, the hearing commenced and the last witness to testify was red-headed and red-cheeked JH.

Here is a verbatim transcript of the trial dialogue:

Mort: "JH, isn't it a fact that you have been advised that you have active TB?"

JH: "Yeah."

Mort: "Isn't it a fact that you have been advised that if you didn't take your TB medication that you would be a danger to the community?"

[2] A small controlled space with two doors. Essentially, one must enter the space and close the first door before opening the second to proceed.

JH: "Yeah, I kinda remember that."

Mort: "Based upon your disease and your noncompliance with your direct observe therapy[3] you were a serious danger to your friends and neighbors, then why won't you agree to be hospitalized until you are cured of this deadly disease?"

Tearfully, JH looked into the Judge's eyes then he dramatically lowered his voice. He started his plea by raising his hands together as if to pray for forgiveness.

JH: "Judge, I have the greatest job of my life. I love it. I can't afford to lose it. I will never get it back."

You could hear a pin drop as we all stood in the Ward D cell, in deathly silence, all anticipating the Judge's next question.

The Judge loudly bellowed: 'Sir, exactly what job do you hold?"

With the same angelic soft tone in his voice JH replied:

JH: "Judge, I run the projector at a Gaiety XXX theatre."

We all bit our tongues in an effort to not burst out laughing. The Judge had the last word.

He looked into JH's eyes and in his best Southern drawl said: "Sorry, my fine man, your rationale, while quite interesting, just isn't compelling enough for you to keep your freedom. Therefore I am ordering you to spend the next 180 days at A.G. Holly Hospital."

As the group exited the hospital they all collectively breathed in the clear cold February air. Their lungs burned as they inhaled. As Mort cleaned his glasses for the third time, he contemplated kicking his tobacco addiction. The others breathed a sigh of relief that the case was over. Despite the inclement weather, the group warmly basked in their knowledge that JH would no longer spread his deadly disease. And knew they would never forget this tragic comedy. ☼

---

3 A process wherein a health care worker meets with the patient and observes the patient taking his tuberculosis medication.

The Alcoholic

By Morton Laitner

My friend Brian was an alcoholic. He was the Health Department's veterinarian. Brian was a kind-hearted, forty-five year old the day we met. He was a handsome man with dyed, jet-black hair and a two pack-a-day habit. His left ear was somewhat deformed and rumor had it that his wife threw boiling water on it when he was in a drunken stupor. Brian could not and did not even try to not hide his weakness. He would come to work with the sweet liquor-odor emanating from his mouth. His breath and his clothes smelled like a smoky bar hours past midnight. He rented a small apartment two blocks away from our offices and three blocks from the Courthouse. Brian's landlord, Miriam, an elderly widow, was also employed as his secretary. She was his security blanket, his surrogate mom and his savior. Miriam made sure Brian left for work on time, that his paperwork was complete, and that he attended the weekly intercom meeting.

As the Department's vet, Brian was required to testify in rabies cases. As counsel for the agency, I would ask him the standard preliminary questions:

Please state your name.

Please state your business address.

Please state your occupation.

Are you licensed in Florida as a veterinarian?

How long have you been so licensed?

Then I would inquire:

What is rabies?

Are raccoon's known vectors of rabies?

Have there been rabid raccoons recently located in Dade County?

How do you test a raccoon for rabies?

Do you have a recommendation for this court as to what should be done with this raccoon?

What is that recommendation?

We had run this trial routine successfully on numerous occasions with no hitches. Now, one-hell-of-a-hitch arrived before our 9:00 AM hearing. Brian was supposed to be in his office by eight. Miriam arrived at 8:05 in tears, waving her hands in front of her face like a bee was about to sting her on the nose. She cried out, "Brian is totally blotto. He's dressed, but I couldn't yank him out of bed. What are we going to do? This will cost him his job!"

Think fast!

What would Perry Mason do?

Move into action, no time to panic.

Miriam and I ran over to Brian's apartment. While Miriam brewed the Maxwell House, I lifted Brian out of bed. Brian groggily said, "I need a shot of vodka". I responded, "Sorry, Brian. We are going to court today." With Brian's arm wrapped around my shoulder we paced back and forth from one end of the apartment to the other. I yelled, "Miriam, Brian's capable of walking". Miriam pumped four cups of coffee down Brian's throat. As the three of us rushed to the Courthouse, I repeatedly instructed Brian, "I'm only going to ask you questions that require you to say 'yes'. Brian, do you understand?" Brian replied, "Yes." Luckily, we made it to the judge's chambers on time and there was no opposing counsel to object to my leading questions.

Here's how it went after the bite victim and the Health Department physician testified:

Lawyer: You are Dr. Smith, veterinarian for the Health Department?

Brian: Yes.

Lawyer: Are raccoon's known vectors of rabies?

Brian: Yes.

Lawyer: Has the Health Department recently found rabid raccoons in Dade County?

Brian: Yes.

Lawyer: Do you recommend to this Court that the raccoon in question raccoon be tested for rabies?

Brian: Yes.

Lawyer: Your Honor, I have no further questions of this witness and I rest the Department's case.

The court ruled in favor of testing the raccoon.

I looked over at Miriam. She smiled back at me knowing that we had saved Brian's job for another day. I thought to myself, Mason could not have done it any better.

Postscript: Within one year of this incident, Miriam left the Health Department. Brian lost his job within one week of her retirement.

This story is a work of fiction. Names, characters, places and incidents are products of the author's imagination or are used fictitiously. Any resemblance to actual events or locales or persons, living or dead, is entirely coincidental. ☼

Now, For the Rest of the Story...

By Michael McCullom

Twenty-five years later Brian stands before a crowded room. At the podium he proclaims, "My name is Brian and I am an alcoholic." He tells the listeners of what his life was like, what happened, and how his life is now.

He starts by telling his peers the hell he lived for so many years while under the influence of alcohol. He reviews the many nights that he had promised himself and others that he would stop drinking. He remembers days he had let so many of them down. He shares how people would try to help him and how much a woman named Miriam was always there to pick up the pieces. He continues to tell how he had lost many jobs and friends and ended up in hospitals and jails. But nothing could stop him from drinking.

Then he tells what happened one night. This night, 25 years ago today, was no different than any other night. Brain was drinking heavily; he was sitting alone on the floor drinking a bottle of Smirnoff Vodka (second one of the day). In his left hand was a 45 caliber pistol, in the other hand his family Bible. He thought, "The Vodka is not working any more; it will not take away my fears nor my pain." He went on to say, "I can not get drunk nor get sober." The gun, he admits, was just a fearful option and he could not really end his life. So he picked up the Bible and shouted, "If there is a God, please help me! Help me now!" At that moment he heard an inner voice. The voice instructed him, "Pick up the phone and call Alcoholic Anonymous."

That night, as lonely and terrifying a night he had ever had, was the supreme turning point of his life. A night he will never forget.

From the platform Brian continues to tell his story. All eyes in the crowded room stare at him with hope, courage and strength. He shares, "I have not had a drink in 25 years." He goes on to say, "I found a new way of living and new friends – friends that have given me the tools so as to not pick up the first drink." He says to his peers, "It's the first drink that gets you drunk. And that first drink would land me back into a life of self destruction; a Hell I never want to see again."

He shares how he now lives a life of honesty, open-mindedness, and willingness to do God's will. He explains how he uses his misfortunes to better himself and others. Brian gives details of his going back and making amends with Miriam for the way he took advantage of her kindness. He found her old, frail and alone only to take her back into his home and help her live out her last few months in dignity. He tells of how this year he will retire from working at a nonprofit animal shelter and will travel with his wife of 22 years after his daughter leaves for college. He finishes by saying, "I don't even think about drinking anymore but I know in order to remain sober I must not drink, I should help others and keep God close to my heart." Brian lowers his head and tells everyone that they to could change their lives and have peace and serenity too.

Brian thanks the crowd and leaves wishing only one thing, that one day he will find his old friend from the Department of Health and tell him the rest of the story. ☼

REMEMBER this story remains work of fiction. Names, characters, places and incidents are products of the author's imagination or are used fictitiously. Any resemblance to actual events or locales or persons, living or dead, is entirely coincidental.

Michael McCullon works for the State Bureau of Immunization as a Management Consultant.

High Hopes

By Morton Laitner

"I am covered in sweat.

What a nightmare!

Where am I?"

"Oh yeah, the Fontainebleau, Presidential Suite, fifteenth floor." Lying in bed, the bright sun streaming through the glass windows, blinding his old blue eyes. He looked out onto the large balcony with a view of miles of blue Atlantic waters. Frank thought, "I drank too much Jack last night; it's too damn hot for December." He lit his first Marlboro, his throat burned as he inhaled the white smoke. "I had better kick this damn habit before I lose my voice and my career."

Leaning over the crystal ashtray, filled with cigarette butts and memories of another crazy night, he grabbed for the hotel pen and stationary. He quickly scribbled down his fast-fading memories of the troubling dream.

It was the early 30's.

Hoboken, New Jersey.

His fifteen year-old cousin Regina.

Lying in her mother's bed with TB.

Skinny, fevers, night sweats.

Coughing her guts out.
Begging God to take her away.
Family all broken up.
Crying their eyes out.
The priest giving Regina her last rights.
Frank stopped scribbling. He mused, "What the hell does that dream mean? Was this a message from above? Was he in need of a penance to avoid purgatory for his partying? Did Regina want him to do something?"

As Frank got dressed, putting on his brown linen trousers, his silk shirt, his signature thin tie and fedora, he made a decision. He reached for the gold-plated phone and called his personal assistant into the room. Amy entered and heard Frank say in a soft, worn out voice, "Babe, I want you to make arrangements for me to perform a free concert at a TB hospital. Let me know when the gig is booked." Amy called the Lantana TB hospital. Upon hearing the news the administrator exclaimed, "This will be the best holiday gift for the patients and the staff! Thank the Chairman of the Board for me."

The next morning when Frank woke up, he felt better than he had in years. Sinatra thought to himself, "WOW! So this is what 9:00 a.m. on a Tuesday looks like!" Climbing into the black Cadillac stretch-limo with his swinging ensemble, they left the hotel and headed North on US1 to Lantana.

Frank thought to himself, "Doesn't that young Senator from Massachusetts, what the hell was his name? Something Kennedy, the one with the good-looking wife. Doesn't his dad own a compound in Palm Beach? If they're there, I'd like to stop by and see them." But before Sinatra could ask the chauffeur if he knew where the compound was, he pictured Regina's sickly face. Frank realized he was on a mission!

A mission to make patients smile and forget their troubles.

A holy mission that was sent via a dream by an angel named Regina.

A mission for which he would not seek any publicity.

As Frank and his entourage arrived at the distinguished hospital, he saw a tent covering two hundred chairs and a banner that read, "WELCOME FRANK! WE LOVE YOU!" Frank toured the hospital with the Chief Medical Physician, shaking hands, giving encouragement to the patients some of whom would, unfortunately, be confined to their beds for the show, but would hear him through their open windows.

Frank took to the stage, grabbed the microphone and sat on a white wooden stool. Then he told the audience about his dream. The audience responded like bobby soxers. Frank knew the song he would sing to the patients. A song that would lift their spirits and give them hope. His band struck up the first note to "High Hopes." Frank began to sing:

"Next time you are found,
with your chin on the ground,
there is a lot to be learned,
so look around.
Just what makes that little old ant
Think he'll move that rubber tree plant
Anyone knows an ant, can't
Move a rubber tree plant."

When he reached the chorus everyone joined in:
"Cause he got high hopes,
He's got high hopes,
He's got high, apple pie
In the sky hopes."

When Sinatra concluded, there was a three-minute standing ovation. Franks eyes teared as he looked into the audience and remembered cousin Regina. He was humming "High Hopes" as he got into his limo.

He felt good about himself as the black limo cruised down I-95, headed back to Miami Beach. Tonight he and Dean, Sammy, Joey, Peter – the whole rat-pack – would cavort on the hotel stage to a healthier audience.

On the stage that night, Frank was covered in sweat. A cigarette was dangling out of his mouth as he took a sip from his glass of Jack Daniels. Frank smiled as he thought about his long day. He knew his life was a dream and where it was taking him. He had done his penance. An angel smiled upon him.

He had "High Hopes." ✺

Editor's Notes:
This fictionalized account is based on an actual event.

If by chance you get the opportunity to visit the AG Holley Hospital in Lantana, go to the third floor and you will see a picture of Frank Sinatra visiting with the patients at the hospital.

Oh Rats

By Frederick Villari and Morton Laitner

I t was a red hot September afternoon, Frederick, a young attorney who had just began practicing for the Health Department sat as comfortably as possible in his undersized cubicle thinking about his upcoming lunch of chili con carne. Fred had worked for the State Attorney's Office Delinquent Child Support Unit. While working there, he enjoyed going after so-called men who shirked their financial responsibility to their own children. He considered them vermin.

Fred's blackberry rang; it played a Red Hot Chili Pepper tune. On the line was an anxious, crying, elderly female, nick-named Minnie. She wept as she blurted out, "My dog (You guessed it, Pluto) had been bitten by a mean dirty rat!" Minnie was currently at her vet's office seeking care for her beloved pet. She angrily exclaimed, "I have had it with Marvin!" Marvin was her so-called animal-loving neighbor, for the past ten years. Minnie yelled into her I-phone, "The whole neighborhood is up-in-arms because Marvin's rats are everywhere." Minnie not only feared for her dog's safety, but also feared that these rats would spread disease. Fred reassured her in his best James Cagney voice, "Minnie, the Health Department will get those dirty rats."

Fred started drafting a sanitary nuisance complaint. He would get the neighbors to write affidavits describing the vermin problem. Here are some of the neighbor's quotes taken directly from their affidavits.

1. I was walking my rat-terrier dog in my back yard when my dog came out of the bushes with a dead rat in her mouth and mark bites on her chest. I immediately took my dog to the veterinarian who told me that my dog suffered from rat bites. Approximately four months ago I looked over the fence into Marvin's backyard and witnessed approximately twenty rats running around his property. They were scurrying along his fence and the entire backyard. I have personally witnessed Marvin himself feeding the rats in his backyard at least fifteen different times.

2. Almost every morning I see fresh rat droppings on the rear-sliding glass door and at my front door. I have also seen rat droppings on my patio and in my garage. I have personally killed approximately twenty-five rats on my property.

3. For approximately one year I have seen rats crossing my backyard fence daily. My dogs have killed at least fifteen, if not more, rats, most of them white in color, the others lighter brown in color. One rat was discovered at the bottom of my pool.

4. I now have an 18 month old granddaughter that I care for and a second grandchild on the way. I have outdoor play toys and activity sets in my backyard. I fear allowing my granddaughter to play in the backyard due to the rat problem.

5. I, as well as my husband, am extremely fearful and afraid for our safety.

6. One rat came into my house through an open door. I was able with the help of my husband to chase the rat out of my house. I am personally terrified and have constant nightmares of the rats. My experience with the rats has left me traumatized and I fear the rats may bite me or my dog.

Next, Fred phoned Marvin to hear his side of the story. Marvin explained, "My home is a drop-off point for people who abandon their dogs, cats and even their pet pink-eyed-white (PEW) rats."[Editors note: We are not making this up, Google it.] "This infestation is not my fault." Marvin intoned.

While Fred listened to Marvin, the Red Hot Chili Peppers' tune got stuck in his brain. "Give it away, give it away, give it away now." Fred thought about people like Marvin and the dead-beat dads, who would rather give away their problems than face the responsibility for their actions. He had seen them too often in his line of work.

Then Marvin boldly announced his plan, "How about the Health Department trapping these beautiful creatures in animal-friendly cages. Then I'll pay to ship them off to my 2,000 acre farm in Alabama." Fred mentally pictured the dreaded call from the Governor of Alabama. The Governor would drawl "Young man, why y'all sending Florida rats to retire in my sweet home Alabama?" Not wanting to start a battle between neighboring states, Fred rejected the offer.

Fred now had to come up with a theme for the case. He remembered his childhood church-going days, when the parish priest preached about the biblical "Good Neighbor". He had found his theme.

Fred would tell the Judge that this animal-loving Marvin had forgotten that his good neighbors were also part of the animal kingdom.

Fred phoned Marvin announcing, "I'm ready to go to court."

Marvin capitulated, "I give up. I surrender. I will sign a pest-control contract to eradicate the rats from my property."

Fred, for the first time in his new career, had tasted the sweet flavor of Health Department justice.

The rats would die. Minnie, her dog Pluto, and Marvin's other neighbors would be safe and happy again. And a new tune would sound inside Fred's head. And like a good neighbor, the Health Department was there. ☼

Poster issued by State Board of Health to promote rat eradication campaign of the 1920's.[4]

TRAP RATS.
OBEY THE JUST SANITARY LAW.
HAVE YOUR PREMISES CLEANED
THIS IS YOUR DUTY.

4 William J. Bigler, Public Health in Florida - Yesterday: Florida's Public Health Centennial, Florida Journal of Public Health, Vol, 1, No. 3, May 1989, p.7-19

A Blessing

By Morton Laitner

I glanced out the large glass door of my home and observed a heavenly mist floating three feet above the lake. A wintery wind swirled the mist into tight mini tornadoes. This visual blessing reminded me of another blessing that occurred one year earlier. Here's the tale.

As counsel for the Health Department I have a myriad of responsibilities. One of them is to seek the revocation or suspension of licenses of septic tank contractors. Some of these contractors fail to complete a job after securing a substantial deposit.

One notorious company, Snidley Septic Tank Contractors had secured a five-thousand dollar deposit from Miss Nell Fenwick. After months of trying and failing to get her septic system installed or the return of her money, Nell approached the Health Department for assistance. I met sweet Nell in my office. I felt her pain. She cried as she told me that the money represented most of her life savings. After calling Snidely and leaving a message on their line, I sent our demand letter with the usual warning: Either you return the money to Nell or we're going after your contractor's license.

Two weeks later, when I handed Nell a certified check in the amount of five-thousand dollars, tears of joy dripped down her face.

She exclaimed, "God Bless the Health Department!"

I smiled back at Nell and said, "Nell, health department employees get praised once in a while, but when one of our customers calls on the higher power to bless us, we are truly blessed. Thanks for your kind words."

I opened the glass door and stepped into the wintery chill. As I approached the lake the mist had started to burn off. But my heart was warmed by the memory of sweet Nell's blessing. ☼

Filling the Big Man's Shoes

By J.D. Shingles and Roland Pierre

It was a typical balmy, early December day when the Health Department's Saint Nick, JD, started his annual toy drive to take care of the less fortunate. JD sat in his cubicle listening to one of his favorite Country Christmas song, "Christmas Shoes," by Bob Carlisle.

JD pictured himself standing in front of an eight year old Haitian-American boy, wearing worn-out rags, waiting in a K-mart line anxiously holding a pair of red women's shoes. And when the eight-year-old was ready to pay, JD heard him say to the cashier:

Monsieur, I wanna buy these shoes for ma Mère. It's Christmas Eve and these shoes are just her size. Could you hurry, please? Mon Père says there's not much time. You see, she's been very sick, and I know these shoes will make her smile. I want her to look beautiful if she goes to heaven tonight.

As JD watched the boy counting his pennies, the cashier says, "Sorry, it is not enough." The boy made eye contact with JD and said, "Ma Mère made Christmas good at our home. Most years Ma Mère did without. Tell me, Monsieur. What am I gonna do? Somehow I've got to buy her these Christmas shoes."

Knowing he had to help out, JD pictured laying the additional money down.

J.D. came back to reality from his daydream. He would again be the Health Department's Saint Nick, collecting toys for children who were spending their holiday in hospital beds, or dying of AIDS, or who recently arrived in the country with just the worn out old rags on their backs.

J.D. knew he could count on his Santa helpers: the Boy Scouts, the teenage girl (who gave up her birthday presents so poor children with AIDS would have a more joyous holiday), and the Health Department employees.

A day before Christmas, J.D. donned his Santa suit and rode in his red SUV with antlers attached to the doors, joined by his three Health Department elves, Gert, Ninfa and Roland. They took bags full of toys to Notre Dame Church, where hundreds of children eyed the Christmas tree display. "Ooooh's" and "Aaaah's" spilled from little ones' lips; mothers and fathers eyes widened in surprise of the gifts. "This is just fantastic," said one father. Another parent agreed, "It's wonderful for the kids."

As Santa J.D. poised himself against one of the tables, another group entered. A frantically crying baby approached Santa. The infant, Marie, was irritated. As crying Marie became louder, Santa J.D. became agitated. J.D. asked the mother if he could hold baby Marie. The mother gave permission, and he reached out for the howling baby. At first, Marie hesitated and then she stared at Santa with weeping eyes, leaned forward with "dampened-thumb" as if to say, "Here I am." She continued to wail as Santa cradled her in his arms; she laid her head on his shoulder. There was silence and Santa breathed a sigh of relief. Marie moved in his arms as if she was reaching for something. He turned to see what was happening; she lifted up as he turned away from the toys to see what had caused her to move in his arms. To his surprise, Marie was pointing toward a white teddy bear. Immediately, J.D. grabbed the animal and gave it to her. Marie's silence continued as Santa handed the baby and the teddy bear back to Mommy.

We at the Health Department are blessed to have a man worthy enough to fill Santa's shoes, teaching us the meaning of giving.

As Tears Go By

By Morton Laitner

Hey Bud, I'm your Orange Bowl and don't ya forget it.

I can't believe what I've read online.

I'm going to be demolished next year.

YOU GOTTA BE KIDDING!

Just in case, I'm writing my obituary for publication in "Healthy Stories '08".

I've selected Healthy Stories because I've done so much for the health of South Florida.

You jokers owe me big time.

Remember the JMH Alamo? They saved her.

RENOVATE DON'T DETONATE!

Buddy, ever hear of community mental health?

I invented it.

I'm your mental health poster child.

Let me remind you how I lifted your spirits in '71 and '72.

The undefeated season. 17-0.

We won the Super Bowl.

58 UM home games in a row.

You wouldn't have laid a finger on me back then.

The dolphin jumping out of the tank after every touchdown.

The 1983 National Championship game—The Canes beat the Cornhuskers.

You'll never forget about it.

But you have forgotten about me!

And boy did I make you happy! I felt the tears of joy dripping down your reddened cheeks.

You were all there. Try to remember.

Please change your mind.

I'm your Orange Bowl.

I was born during the Great Depression in '37

I was your NEW Deal; I gave you jobs, hope and a home when you needed me.

For seventy years I have held you in good times and in bad.

My Roman Stadium Cousin is over 2000 years old.

Buddy, fix me but don't destroy me. Please let me be.

Remember the Marial boatlift?

I housed those unfortunates for your protection not mine.

I cried with you when President Kennedy spoke to us after the Bay of Pigs.

But where are your tears for me, Miami?

Didn't I have you moon-walkin' with that kid who wore that one glittering glove?

I'm thinking about all those sad Stones songs that echoed within my walls.

"Time ain't on my side" – Couldn't have said it better.

"Ain't too proud to beg" – I am begging.

"As tears go by" – and I am cryin'.

"It's all over now"

LEAVE ME ALONE!

I'm an historic structure.

My Rival Football Stadiums have become National Historic Landmarks.

Don't you want to be associated with Yale, Harvard, the Rose Bowl and the L.A. Coliseum?

I am slightly younger, but much better looking than those guys!

Please give me one more chance.

Lift me and my spirits up and move me to Homestead.

I protected you!

Now – PLEASE PROTECT ME!

Remember the bio-terrorism field exercise?

I was ready to fight smallpox, SARS and avian influenza as your quarantine facility.

Even today you're using my parking spaces while you build your new Center for Excellence.

Now that I've completed my obit, I realize that there is no hope.

So on the day of my demolition, I want every member of the Miami Health community to raise their frosted mug of Bud …

No make it a Bud Lite (See I am still thinking about your health) and make the following farewell toast.

It's the last call for me.

OB we'll miss you.

OB we loved ya.

OB we'll always remember ya.

Vaya con Dios mi estadio. ☀

Editors's Note:
At the time of publication, OBS had been completely torn down, the only reminders of this historic landmark is the giant boards, bowl bar and the exit sign from the highway.

In the Heat of Passion

By Morton Laitner

Walter was dying of AIDS.

Walt had an unfulfilled dream of visiting the Metro Zoo before his demise. He wanted to see the zebras, giraffes, monkeys and, most of all, the two albino Bengal tigers.

It was the mid-80's and the life expectancy of a person with AIDS was less than two years. The drugs that prolonged victims' lives had not been discovered, and scientists were working around the clock to find a cure.

The newspaper obituary page grew on a daily basis. Unstated causes took the lives of thousands of young men... polite society's way of protecting the living.

Walter lived in Miami, where he had been tested for many things. One of these tests said he had an IQ of 68. This score was derived from several standardized tests which "attempted" to measure his intelligence: the key word being attempted. His Street Q was well within normal limits, as was his knack for expressing his emotions.

Walter was a 21-year-old male. He was jobless and, therefore, always broke. However, he had the optimal living situation for a hot-blooded young male, a co-ed group home: where Walter found lots of time for lots of monkey business.

Now that Walter had tested positive for HIV and had converted to full-blown AIDS, he could no longer remain in this co-ed group home. A hearing was scheduled to get the Court's approval to find a new placement which would properly care for him. The Health Department worked hard to create a special home for AIDS-infected males like Walt. To protect the community, the Health Department also worked hard to educate Walt about using condoms.

The Judge asked: "Walt, where do you want to live?"

Walt roared, "Metro Zoo, I've never been there Judge – but I hear the animals run free. The place ain't got no cages."

The Judge smiled and said to me, "Please proceed with your cross-examination."

Q: Walt, how are you feeling today?
A: Fine.

Q; Have you been to a doctor recently?
A: Yup.

Q: Did the doctor tell you that you have a medical problem?
A: Yup.

Q: Walt, do you have a disease?
A: Yup. I got AIDS.

Q: Do you know how that disease is spread?
A: Yup.

Q: Walt, how is AIDS spread?
A: I don't want to say the word in court.

Q: Do you know how to stop spreading AIDS?
A: Yup.

Q: How?
A: Put on a rubber.

Q: Have you been taught how to put a rubber?
A: Yup.

Now for my sixty-four thousand dollar question, "Walt, the next time you have sex are you going to put on a rubber?"

Walt placed his hand on his chin pausing to think before he answered.

He looked the Judge square in the eyes and whispered, "Judge, in the heat of passion, I can't stop and put one on."

Flabbergasted, everyone in the courtroom sat mesmerized, digesting this nugget of truth that flew from the mouth of this lost soul. Walt had an Achilles heal – lack of self-control. We all knew people with low self-control quotients, and we dreaded picturing them in this plague's death march.

Because of what Walter said, the Judge concurred with the Department's position that he be housed in all male group home with others suffering the same disease.

After the Court's ruling, not wanting Walt to hear, I whispered into the ear of to his young attorney, "Let's surprise Walt with a trip to the zoo."

She gave me the "look" – a quizzical glance that said, "Is that what attorneys do?"

The next day we picked up Walt at his new group home. Walt was totally amazed. While driving to the zoo, we talked about the animals he wanted to see: zebras, giraffes, monkeys, and most of all, two albino Bengal Tigers. We made loud animal noises and acted like chimps bending our elbows and pretending to scratch our underarms with our hands.

At the zoo, we ate sticky cotton candy that melted on our tongues. Our teeth got stuck in caramel apples, and we munched on freshly popped, overly salted popcorn.

Walt smiled and his eyes lit up as he stared, mesmerized, in front of his favorite animals.

On the way home, Walt howled, "This was the best day of my life! Thank you! Did you see those albino tigers? Did you see how those monkeys acted? They just did what they wanted to do with no concern for anything or anybody!"

I could not reply to his questions, as my tears choked my vocal chords. As he got out of my car, I said, "Walt, thanks for giving me an unforgettable day."

I never saw Walt again. I heard from his lawyer that he passed away six months after our trip to the zoo. I imagined his obit and the words that appeared in my mind were, "He died because of a lack of self-control." ☼

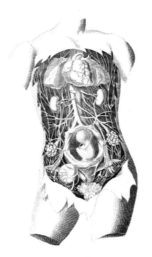

Bodies

By Tracie Dickerson

As I milled about on Las Olas Boulevard, I eyed a "Bodies Exhibit" banner flapping in the breeze. Throughout my stroll I had been people watching. I thought about how men and women are different, and yet the same. I thought about my public health career, and what I have learned about the human body. Because of my job, I have studied lungs (TB), reproductive system (STDs), and the brain (rabies). But before I had this knowledge, I was just a student, spending my summer studying in London.

The first time I heard about the BODIES exhibit I was riding on the "Tube". My Brit-boyfriend told me about his trip to the exhibit and how great it was.

In his adorable British accent, he clamored, "I know it is not your cup of tea love, but it is miraculous."

I was repulsed as he described how the human body had been painstakingly preserved, dissected and posed to best show the human body in motion – only without skin. I was disturbed.

"Zack, you have lost your mind. I should end our relationship right now, before you become the next Jack the Ripper!" Therein lies one of the differences between men and women, I thought to myself.

A few years, a few boyfriends and a few thousand miles across the pond later, I found myself having a similar conversation with another boyfriend, Roy.

"Gross. Not again." I thought to myself.

"What is it about boys and dead bodies? Is there some internal drive they have to poke at dead things with sticks?" I asked Roy.

Eventually, I came around to the idea of taking Roy to the exhibit... mostly because I couldn't come up with anything else I could give him for his birthday. I was tired of gift certificates to the comic book store, and this seemed like something we could enjoy together.

He was overwhelmingly delighted. Though I wasn't excited, I smiled and bought our tickets.

Having grown up in Galveston, a small city with a large teaching hospital, I have seen my fair share of human bodies preserved in jars. I was truly expecting to have a similar experience. Giant jars of pickled people. But the exhibit was much more fascinating.

This exhibit had no jars, but instead was full of people, polymer preserved, but people none the less. I was interested, but still grossed out. There were hundreds of people around me, all had similar reactions to the bodies on exhibit. I stood there for a few minutes chatting with a worker. One of her most frequently asked questions turned out to be, "Are they real?"

Although mildly fascinated by the exhibit, I found myself disinterested after the first few rooms. Roy, however, moved a bit more slowly. Digesting each new part with a vigor I had never seen, I continued to move through the exhibit, staring at some stuff, reading bits here and there... and then I came to the room of dead babies.

Having not had a child yet, I was torn. Do I see the room of babies in different stages, preserved for all time, or skip it and go to the next thing? I went for the room. I was sad as I stared at the display. It was something I may never forget.

I found myself most interested in the human circulatory system. They had colored the veins blue and red, and different parts of the system were so intricate and so beautiful. I had never been more amazed. For the first time I viewed the human body as a piece of art. Not just any art, but more impressive than the entire Louvre kind of art.

When I was done, I bought the exhibit's book for Roy, as an additional birthday present. I waited for another hour and a half as he toured the exhibit, reading the signs, truly learning from the exhibit.

I found a place to have a soda and a cookie, inadvertently assuming a Rodinesque posture, and thought about boys around the world and their fascination with the human form. Some things never change. ☼

Bonus Section

The Editors are proud to present to our Healthy Stories readers this Bonus Section. This section highlights the best stories of Healthy Stories 2007 in three languages. (English, Spanish, Creole). South Florida has become a trilingual community and the workforce of the Miami-Dade County Health Department reflects this. We are fortunate to have Editors with exceptional translating skills. Our employees have been highly complimentary as to our translators finding the right words to convey the resonance of the story. We will continue our trilingual marketing via radio, TV and community newspapers our vignettes. We are proud to be a leader in understanding the need to communicate with everyone in our diverse community.

We wish our readers:
Good health;
Buena Salud and
Bon Suente.

The "Dead" Letter Bin

(A Health Department Mystery)

It's Thursday mid-afternoon, the day before New Year's. The Miami Dade County Health Department is winding down. Many employees are already on leave. Others are fleeing work a little early to get a jump on the extended holiday weekend. At the Administrator's Office, folks are in a festive mood – only a few hours to go 'til quitten' time. The day has been routine – no problems, no crises. Ahhh.

Like every other work day, the postal worker has just arrived with the afternoon's mail. The holiday season has made today's collection of envelopes and small packages lighter than usual. It's an added bonus for the secretary who begins to sort today's delivery. She smiles. Other than the lighter than usual mood and the lighter than usual mail delivery – good things both – it has been an otherwise exceptionally quiet, blissfully uneventful day.

One package stands out among the mail. It is large but not exceedingly so – about 14 inches to a side. But it is odd. It has no mailing label. A secretary picks up and inspects the rather sloppy writing slanting across one side. Something turns over ominously inside. Her brow furrows as she reads. She tenses suddenly and quickly puts the package down. The contented smile is gone, replaced by a very troubled frown. She picks up her phone and punches buttons rapidly. She is getting that sinking feeling that the day's ordinariness and quiet is about to be shattered.

Miles away, in his office, the Health Department legal team gathers around a speaker phone. The attorney grabs a pen and legal pad and starts to scribble furiously. A mysterious parcel has arrived by mail at the Administrator's Office. The box bears no mailing label, no stamps and no postmark. The Health Department's name and address have been scribbled directly on the cardboard in black magic marker. The box has no return address and something hefty and solid inside jostles around when the package is moved. The secretary explains that another inscription has been scrawled in red magic marker beneath the Health Department's name and address. The attorney stops writing and blinks as she reads aloud: "Found loose in the Mails. CREMATED REMAINS."

Now it's the attorney's turn to wear the troubled frown. And like the secretary, he is dialing as fast as he can. Police and postal authorities are alerted and appropriate Agency personnel advised. Employees are ordered to evacuate the Administrator's Office. Police summon a HAZMAT team, who test the parcel for radiological and chemical contamination – both negative. The parcel is whisked away to the State Laboratory for further testing for infective agents.

An hour later, the evacuated personnel are discussing the matter with police outside the Administrator's now-abandoned offices. Employees teem around – some with anxious faces. Everyone wants to help, but there is very little to be done but wait. And everyone is waiting for the laboratory results. When they arrive, a collective sigh of relief seems to escape from all concerned. All is deemed well. The box's contents are just what the box's handwritten inscription claimed them to be – a smaller box containing cremated remains.

Information contained in the box allows Health Department employees to Google-track the package back to South Carolina, where the deceased had lived. Inquiries to a South Carolina cremation society reveal that the deceased's remains had been shipped to a New York funeral home. Further inquiries revealed that, from New York, the remains had been shipped again to the bereaved family in New Jersey. It was during this last and final leg of the trip to return the deceased to his family that the remains were lost. It was a simple matter of an envelope containing the death certificate and affixed to the box coming loose. Apparently, when the United States Postal Service investigated the now-unidentifiable package, the

Miami-Dade County Health Department's name and address had been found inside on an advertisement listed as an important web link. A postal worker must have decided that the Health Department would be better suited to handle the situation, and simply forwarded the parcel – cremated remains and all – to MDCHD.

When the all-clear signal was given, police allow the area to be reopened and employees to return to their offices to pick up their personal things, turn off computers and close up for the weekend. Despite the holiday weekend having begun, the mood in the Administrator's Office could no longer be described as festive. Tired, relieved and thankful would be better descriptions.

This may sound like an upcoming episode of CSI Miami. But this was a real life incident that occurred on December 30, 2004, at the Miami-Dade County Health Department. And it poses a serious question: What would you do, as an employee of the Department of Health, if such a parcel arrived at your desk?

Health Departments have protocols for suspicious packages. Remember the action you must take if a suspect parcel arrives: 1) Do not open or even touch the package if it can be helped; 2) Evacuate the area; 3) Immediately contact law enforcement and postal authorities; and 4) Contact your county health department's safety officer.

Not long ago, the anthrax deaths in Palm Beach County brought to bear the importance of proper screening and securing of the U.S. Mail. This incident underscores that even in the absence of an imminent threat from contaminated mail, Health Department employees must remain vigilant in their observance of proper procedures to identify and secure suspect mail.

The Happy Ending: After talking to the South Carolina cremation society and the New York funeral home, the Health Department returned the cremated remains to the son of the deceased. ☼

El Recipiente de
los Paquetes Devueltos
(Un Misterio del Departamento de Salud)

Spanish translation by Ninfa Urdaneta.

E s jueves en la tarde, el día antes de la víspera de año nuevo. El Departamento de Salud del Condado de Miami-Dade está bajando el ritmo de trabajo. Muchos empleados están ya de vacaciones. Otros se están fugando del trabajo un poco antes para empezar temprano el fin de semana largo. En la Oficina del Administrador, la gente está en un ambiente festivo – solo a unas horas de irse del trabajo. El día ha sido rutinario – sin problemas, sin crisis. Ahhh.

Como de costumbre, el cartero ha acabado de llegar con el correo de la tarde. La temporada festiva ha hecho la recolección de correo del día de hoy más liviana que usualmente. Esto es un bono adicional para la secretaria que comienza a repartir el correo del día de hoy. Ella sonríe. Aparte del humor más ligero que usualmente y del correo más ligero que usualmente – ambas buenas cosas – ha sido un día silencioso y felizmente tranquilo.

Un paquete destaca de entre el correo. Es un paquete grande pero no excesivamente grande – alrededor de 14 pulgadas cada lado. Pero es raro. No tiene etiqueta de dirección. La secretaria lo agarra e inspecciona el bastante descuidado escrito inclinado de un extremo al otro en uno de los lados. Algo amenazadoramente da vuelta adentro. Sus cejas se fruncen mientras lee. Repentinamente se tensa y suelta el paquete. La sonrisa sostenida se ha ido y es reemplazada por un ceño fruncido. Ella coge el teléfono y marca números rápidamente. Ella está teniendo el mal presentimiento de que la normalidad del día y el silencio están a punto de hacerse añicos.

A millas de distancia, en su oficina, los miembros del equipo legal se reúnen alrededor del teléfono de altavoz. El abogado agarra un bolígrafo y un bloc de papel tamaño legal y comienza a hacer garabatos furiosamente. Un misterioso paquete ha llegado por correo a la Oficina de Administración. No tiene etiqueta de dirección, ni estampillas ni matasellos. El nombre y dirección del Departamento de Salud han sido garabateados directamente sobre el cartón con marcador mágico negro. La caja no tiene dirección de domicilio para respuesta y algo pesado y sólido adentro empuja de un lado a otro cuando el paquete es movido. La secretaria explica que otra inscripción ha sido garabateada en marcador rojo mágico abajo del nombre y dirección del Departamento de Salud. El abogado deja de escribir y parpadea mientras ella lee en voz alta: "Encontrado suelto en el correo. RESTOS CREMADOS."

Ahora le toca al abogado fruncir el ceño. E igual que la secretaria, él está marcando tan rápido como él puede. La Policía y las Autoridades Postales son alertadas y el personal apropiado de la Agencia ha sido informado. Los empleados son mandados a salir de la Oficina de Administración. La Policía pide la ayuda del equipo HAZMAT, el cual examina el paquete sobre contaminación radiológica y química – ambas negativas. El paquete es llevado rápidamente al Laboratorio del Estado a fin de realizar exámenes adicionales sobre agentes infecciosos.

Una hora después, el personal que ha sido evacuado está discutiendo el asunto con la policía afuera de las ahora abandonadas oficinas de Administración. Los empleados rebosan alrededor – algunos con caras ansiosas. Todos quieren ayudar, pero hay muy poco que hacer aparte de esperar. Y todo el mundo está esperando por los resultados del laboratorio. Cuando ellos llegan, un suspiro de alivio colectivo parece escapar de todos los afectados. Todo se considera que está bien. El contenido de la caja no es más que el que la inscripción a mano indica que es – una caja pequeña conteniendo restos cremados.

La información contenida en la caja permite a los empleados del Departamento de Salud rastrear en Google la procedencia del paquete a South Carolina, donde el difunto había vivido. Consultas a la sociedad de cremación de South Carolina revelan que los restos del difunto habían sido enviados a una funeraria de Nueva York. Investigaciones adicionales revelan que, de Nueva York, los restos habían sido enviados otra vez a la familia de New Jersey que había perdido un ser querido. Fue en este último tramo del viaje destinado a retornar los restos del difunto a su familia que los restos se perdieron. Era un simple caso de un sobre que contenía un certificado de defunción y pegado a la caja que se desprendió. Aparentemente, cuando el Servicio Postal de los Estados Unidos investigó el ahora no identificable paquete, el nombre y dirección del Departamento de Salud del Condado de Miami-Dade habían sido encontradas adentro en un anuncio listado como un importante enlace de Internet. Un trabajador del servicio postal debió haber pensado que el Departamento de Salud era el que mejor podía manejar la situación y simplemente reenvió el paquete – restos cremados y demás – al MDCHD.

Cuando la señal de fin de la alerta fue dada, la policía permite reabrir el área y a los empleados a retornar a sus oficinas a fin de recoger las pertenencias personales, apagar las computadoras y cerrar por el fin de semana. A pesar de que el fin de semana largo había comenzado, el humor en la Oficina de Administración no podía seguir siendo descrito como festivo. Cansado, aliviado, y agradecido sería una mejor descripción.

Esto puede sonar como a un próximo episodio de CSI Miami. Pero esto fue un incidente de la vida real que ocurrió el 30 de Diciembre del 2004, en el Departamento de Salud del Condado de Miami-Dade. Y plantea una importante pregunta: ¿Qué harías tú, como empleado del Departamento de Salud, si tal paquete llegara a tu escritorio?

Los Departamentos de Salud tienen protocolos para paquetes sospechosos. Recuerda la acción que debes tomar si un paquete sospechoso llega: 1) No abras o toques el paquete si es posible; 2) Evacua el área; 3) Inmediatamente contacta a las agencias del orden público y a las autoridades postales; 4) Contacta el funcionario de seguridad del departamento de salud de tu condado.

No hace mucho, las muertes por ántrax en el Condado de Palm

Beach llamaron la atención sobre la importancia de escanear y asegurar el Correo de los Estados Unidos. Este incidente subraya que aún en la ausencia de una inminente amenaza por correo contaminado, los trabajadores del Departamento de Salud deben mantenerse vigilantes en la observancia de los procedimientos apropiados de identificación y seguridad de correo sospechoso.

Un Final Feliz: Después de hablar con la sociedad de cremación de South Carolina y la funeraria de Nueva York, el Departamento de Salud le retornó los restos cremados al hijo del difunto. ☼

Rès Zosman Mò Nan Bwat Pou Resevwa Kourye Ke Lapòst Pote

(Yon mistè nan depatman lasante a)

Creole translation by : Roland R. Pierre, MSMIS, BBA, CISA.

Se te yon Jedi apre midi la vèy joudlan Depatman lasante a pa tap fonksyonnen a plen randman. Anpil anplwaye te an vakans. Lòt yo te ap kite travay la pi bonè pou yo te pwofite vakans long pleying ke jou konje joudlan ajoute ak samdi ak dimanch ta pral ba yo.

Nan biwo administrasyon a lide moun te sou fèt, se te sèlman kèk è de tan avan ke travay te lage. Jou a te ap pase dous san pwoblèm, san tèt chaje. Ahhh!

Tankou nan tout lòt jou travay yo, anplwaye lapòst la te fèk rive ak kourye, (lèt ak bwat lapòst pote) apre midi a. Epòk vakans la te lakòz ke te gen mwens anvlòp ak ti bwat pake ke dabitid. Se te yon bon kado pou sekretè a ki te reskonsab triye kourye sila a jou sa a. Li te ap souri. Si se pate pou de bon bagay: kè kontan ke tout moun te genyen, ak kourye a ki pa te anpil jou sila a li te kab di ke jou sa te yon jou tankou tout lòt jou, yon jou beni san bwi san kont, san okenn tèt chaje

Yon bwat te atire atansyon li nan mitan kourye ke lapòst te pote jou sa a. Li te gwo men li pate vreman twò twò gwo, li te katòz pous nan yon bò. Se te dwòl ke kote bwat la soti a pa te ekri sou li. Yon sekretè ranmase bwat la epi enspekte vyè ekriti panche ki te sou yon bò bwat la. Te genyen yon bagay dwòl ki tap glise andedan bwat la. Sekretè a plise figi li, min li te chanje pandan ke li tap li ekriti ki te sou bwat la. Kò li redi ak laperèz epi byen vit li te depoze bwat la. Yon min figi moun ki nan tèt chaje te rannplase souri ki te sou bouch li a. Li prann telefòn li, li peze bouton yo byen vit. Li santi ke lapè ak ladousè ti jou san bwi san kont san tèt chaje a tap disparèt.

Byen lwen nan yon biwo ekip depatman sante piblik la te rasanble devan yon nan telefòn ki genyen yon mikro sou li. Avoka depatman lasante a rale yon plim ak yon blòk papye long epi li kòmanse ap ekri tankou yon siklòn. Te genyen yon bwat sispèk ki te rive pa lapòst nan biwo administrasyon a. Bwat la pa te genyen yon labèl, ki se yon ti moso papye blan kote yo tape non ak adrès kote bwat la dwe ale, li pa te gen dat ak so lapòst la sou li.Non ak adrès depatman sante piblik la te grafouyen sou bwat la ak yon makè nwa. Non ak adrès moun ki te voye li a pa te sou li non plis epi te genyen yon bagay ki tap sekwe an dedan li lè yo bouje bwat la.. Sekretè a eksplike ke an ba non ak adrès depatman lasante a te genyen yon lòt ekriti yo te grafouyen sou bwat la ak yon makè rouj. Avoka a sispan ekri, li bat popyè je li lè sekretè a te ap li byen fò "bagay nou jwenn gaye nan kourye lapòst la : rès zosman mò."

Kounye a se te tou pa avoka a pou plise fwon li epi fè yon min figi moun ki gen tèt chaje. Tankou sekretè a te fè a, avoka tou komanse peze bouton telefòn pli vit ke li te kapab. Depatman lasante a avèti lapolis, ak otorite lapòst yo osijè de sa ki tap pase a epi tou li avèti otorite tout lòt òganizasyon ki te oblije konnen sa ki tap pase a. Menm moman a yo bay lòd pou tout anplwaye nan biwo administrasyon a kouri kite biwo soti deyò tou swit. Lapolis fè gwoup polisye ki okipe bagay sispèk ki rele HAZMAT kouri vini pou fè tès reyon radioaktif ak tès chimik pou wè si bwat la pa te genyen bagay konsa ki ta kapab kontamine moun. Tout de tès sa yo ke yo te fè te montre ke bwat la pa te genyen pwoblèm. Yo voye bwat la byen vit nan laboratwa leta genyen nan Miyami pou fè tès pou wè si bwat la te genyen mikwòb ki te kapab enfekte moun.

In è de tan apre anplwaye biwo a ke yo ke yo te fè soti deyò tap diskite sa ki te pase a ak lapolis devan bilding la. Anplwaye yo te fè ti pil devan bilding la, anpil nan yo te gen laperèz make sou figi yo. Tout moun te vle ede men pa te genyen anyen ke yo te kab fè eksepte tann. Tout moun tap tann pou rezilta laboratwa yo. Lè rezilta yo rive tout moun respire ak yon gwo soulajman. Tout bagay te nan plas yo,pa te genyen pwoblèm. Sa ki an dedan bwat la se te ekzakteman sa ki te make sou li a - an dedan gwo bwat la yon ti bwat ki te genyen rès zosman yon mò ke yo te boule.

Enfòmasyon ki te nan bwat la te pèmèt ke anplwaye depatman lasante yo te ale nan pati entènèt ki rele Google la pou konnen ke bwat la te soti nan South Carolina kote mò a tap viv. Lè yo fè rechèch yo jwenn ke yon ponp finèb nan South Carolina te voye zosman mò a bay yon ponp finèb nan New-York. Lè yo kontinye chèche yo jwenn ke New-York te voye zosman mò a bay fanmi li ki te nan chagren nan New-Jersey. Se te pandan pati vwayaj soti New-York pou ale New-Jersey a ke zosman mò a ke yo tap voye bay fanmi li te pèdi. Te gen yon bagay byen senp ki te rive, yo te kole yon anvlòp ki te genyen sètifika desè a sou bwat la epi anvlòp la te dekole nan vwayaj a dwat a gòch la. Kòm anvlòp la pa te sou bwat la, lapòst pa te konnen kote pou yo te voye bwat la, li sanble ke lapòst la tap chèche konnen osijè de bwat la lè ke yo jwenn yon papye reklam ak non ak adrès Depatman Lasante nan Miyami. Petèt ke yon anplwaye lapòst la te deside ke depatman lasante a te pi kapab regle sitiyasyon a, epi li senpleman voye bwat la, - zosman mò, ak tout bagay – bay Depatman Lasante nan Miyami.

Lè ke yo di ke tout bagay te rantre nan lòd, lapolis te kite leta ouvri bilding nan pou anplwaye te kab tounen nan biwo yo pou al ranmase zafè yo, eten konpitè yo ak fèmen biwo pou jou konje ki tap vini yo. Malgre fèt la ki te rive sou yo, nou ta di ke anplwaye nan biwo administrasyon an te pèdi kè kontan ke yo te genyen avan nan komansman jounen a. Nou ta di pito ke yo te bouke, yo te soulaje, yo te gen rekonesans.

Tout sa ki pase a te pi sanble yon epizòd sinema CSI Miyami(yon kalite film sispens). Men se te yon istwa tout bon ki te pase nan Depatman Lasante nan Miyami a jou ki te 30 Desanm, 2004. Evenman sa a fè ke nou ap poze yon keksyon enpòtan ? Kòm yon anplwaye depatman lasante a, ki sa ou dwe fè si yon bwat konsa ta rive sou biwo ou?

Depatman lasante genyen règleman ekri ki di tout sa moun dwe fè lè yo resewa yon bwat oswa yon lèt ki sispèk. Sonje byen sa ou dwe fè si yon bwat sispèk vini jwenn ou :1) Otan ke ou kapab, pa manyen oswa louvri bwat la. 2) Soti kite kote bwat la ye a. 3) Rele lapolis ak otorite lapòst yo tou swit. 4) Rele tou swit moun ki ofisye pou sekirite nan depatman lasante ou a.

Pa gen lontan ke maladi chabon ki te lakòz lanmò nan Konte Palm Beach la te fè nou realize kouman li enpòtan pou nou byen tcheke ak byen mete an sekirite bwat oswa lèt ke lapòst pote. Menm lè ke pa te genyen danje kontaminasyon nan bwat la, sa ki te pase jou sa a, montre ke anplwaye depatman lasante yo dwe pou rete vigilan epi swiv règleman ekri ki di tout sa moun dwe fè lè yo resevwa yon bwat oswa yon lèt ki sispèk.

Istwa a byen fini, aprè ke depatman lasante a te pale ak ponp finèb nan South Carolina ak nan New-York yo, li te voye remèt zosman mò a bay pitit gason li. ☀

The Rat Lady

By Mort Laitner

It was another humid, scorching Miami August day in 1985, and Mort sat in his air-conditioned office, thinking about how lucky he was to be inside. After reviewing his schedule, he noticed he had a meeting with a family in the community who had some environmental health concerns. Ronnie & Maria had a complaint about their eighty-two year old neighbor, Grandmother Mary. Mary lived alone for the last forty years in a home surrounded by fruit trees and a chain link fence.

Ronnie and Maria introduced themselves to Mort and promptly presented him with photographs of Grandma Mary's fence. These photographs unmistakably showed the fence shared with Mary and numerous well fed, one and a half foot long Norwegian rats. From his work with Environmental Health, Mort was acutely aware that the Norwegian rat is one of the best known and common rats, and also one of the largest. This type of rat typically lives wherever humans live, particularly in urban areas. Although many rats are beneficial in biological research, Mort knew that wild rats can be extremely dangerous and are directly responsible for the spread of many diseases.

Ronnie & Maria were concerned that their children would be bitten by these huge rodents. They wanted them exterminated immediately. Mort was in agreement. These worried parents were not being overprotective. Rat's teeth that are constantly growing, which causes rats to gnaw any items they come in contact with, keeping their teeth sharp and ready for their next meal. Rats contaminate 10 times as much food as they eat, with urine, droppings and hair. Rats are carriers of at least 10 different kinds of diseases including bubonic plague, murine typhus, spirochetal jaundice, leptospirosis, rabies, rat bite fever, and bacterial food poisoning. A rat bite from even domesticated rats can cause "Rat Bite Fever" which has been fatal in 7-10% of cases. Many times rats bite sleeping children while trying to get bits of food on the child that were not washed off before going to bed. These parents were acting for the good of their children. Mort wondered about the health of the elderly woman living in the home.

Mort knew rats are statutorily considered a sanitary nuisance and the Health Department can take steps ensure the nuisance is abated. He wanted to act quickly on this pressing matter. He developed an action plan. First, he would send out the Health Department photographer to take photos of the house and fence at twilight. Second, he would draft his lawsuit to seek an injunction to eradicate the rodent infestation.

The next day, the Department's crack photographer, Michael Rybolowik, delivered unbelievably graphic photos of numerous rats hanging out in Mary's window sills and at other locations at the property. While Mort studied the photos, he began to picture the worst case scenario:

A process server delivers the lawsuit to Mary. As the elderly woman has the lawsuit read to her, she has a heart attack, and despite great efforts for resuscitation, she dies from shock. The local press is contacted, and Mort is criticized for their improper handling of this case and for the killing of this wonderful cookie-baking grandmother.

This was not an outcome Mort could live with. He decided there must be a better way. He decided before filing a lawsuit, he would instead visit Mary to see if she would cooperate and leave the house while the rats were being eradicated. Mort ventured into the direct sunlight, heat and humidity to see if Mary and he could work out this problem.

As Mort approached Mary's home, he was confronted with his greatest fear of rats. Although his mind was focused on forgetting, with every approaching step to Mary's door, a scene creepy Orwellian scene from the movie, "1984", was on constant replay: A prisoner's greatest fear of rats is successfully exploited as he is tortured in a room full of caged rats. Each time he is not compliant with the torturer's requests, the angry vermin are moved closer and closer to his face. Mort shivered with the memory as he knocked on Mary's door. There was no answer at first; Mort was ready to leave. As he raised his hand to knock on the door a second time, he felt his whole body wanting to run down the steps to the sidewalk and to the safety of the street. Mort pounded his knuckles into the heavy wooden door. The door opened slowly. Before him stood Mary, an extremely frail elderly lady that reminded Mort of his own grandmother. Mort quickly noticed that both of Mary's ankles were wrapped in gauze. He wondered if this gauze was covering the bites from the ever nibbling rats.

Looking beyond the opened door, Mort saw multiple rats scampering across Mary's living room. On the floor was a pan filled with water for the rats to drink, an antique coca cola platter with white bread for the rats to eat. There were rat droppings covering every inch of the floor and furniture.

Mary invited Mort inside her home. The vision of the 1984 tortured prisoner again flashed in Mort's mind. Nothing could have prepared him for what he saw next. As he looked at the living room couch he noticed Mary used the couch as her bed, her pillows resting on one end of the couch. He was disturbed by an oily contour of Mary's head rested as she slept. This oily stain was a "rat run". Rats leave an oily trail in areas they frequent. This rat run showed the rats had pushed their oily body between Mary's head and the wall next to the couch.

Mort now had to make a legal-moral decision.

The legal decision, try to convince Mary to leave her house voluntarily, and if she did not leave voluntary, seek a court order to get her out of this rats nest (which would take at least eight hours). Or order her out of her home without any legal authority.

The moral decision, if Mort waited the eight hours to obtain the injunction, and Mary died of rat bites, he would never be able to sleep peacefully again.

MORT ORDERED MARY OUT OF HER HOUSE.

She said she would move into a local motel. Now Mort had to act fast, find a pest control company that would kill the vermin. Hire exterminators, who would tent the house and pump it full of a rodenticide.

After the tent was removed, the exterminators filled eight Hefty bags with dead rats. Mort calculated that each bag was filled with fifty rats. Ergo, four hundred rats had been living with Mary. The smell of 400 dead rats in 90 degrees Fahrenheit temperature was more than Mort could handle. His mustache was filled with the noisome odor. He went to Burdines (now Macy's) and got some paper strips soaked with perfume which he held under his nose for days on end to kill the smell of the dead rats.

Now that the house had been made rat free, a troop of Boy Scouts came in swept, mopped, polished and disposed of the litter and garbage through out the house. Then the Scouts went the extra mile, and painted every room. Mary was able to move back into her house one week after she moved into the motel.

But, the story does not end here.

One of the Health Department's Environmental Inspectors, Jack Freidan, decided to adopt Mary; he would visit her at least once a week, bring her flowers, drink coffee with her, and constantly insure that the rats did not return. Mary lived in the house for another five years. Until her death, Mort received updates from Jack about Mary's health and safety.

The question Mort get asked most often when he tells this story is, why didn't you commit Mary, and have her placed in a nursing home? Mort answers, that having inspected nursing homes during his career, he thought of them as a place of last resort. He would give his own grandmother another chance to live in her home, and Mary was his grandmother for that hot, humid and scorching August week in 1985. ☼

La Señora de las Ratas

Translated by Ninfa Urdaneta

Era otro húmedo día de Agosto en Miami, de calor abrasador del año 1985, en el cual Mort estaba sentado en su oficina con aire acondicionado, pensando que en la suerte que tenía de estar en ella. Después de revisar su agenda, notó que tenía una reunión con una familia en la comunidad que tenía una preocupación en materia de salud ambiental. Ronnie y María tenían una queja en contra de su vecina de ochentidos, la Abuela Mary.

Mary ha vivido sola durante los últimos cuarenta años en una casa rodeada de árboles frutales y una cerca de ciclón.

Ronnie y María se le presentaron a Mort e inmediatamente le mostraron fotos de la cerca de la Abuela Mary. Estas fotos indiscutiblemente mostraban la cerca compartida con Mary y numerosas ratas noruegas bien alimentadas, de un pie y medio de largo. En virtud de su trabajo con la Oficina de Salud Ambiental, Mort estaba bien conciente que la rata noruega es una de las más conocidas y comunes ratas, y es también una de las más grandes. Este tipo de rata vive típicamente en lugares habitados por el hombre, particularmente en áreas urbanas. Aunque muchas ratas son beneficiosas para estudios biológicos, Mort sabía que las ratas salvajes pueden ser extremadamente peligrosas y son directamente responsables por la trasmisión de muchas enfermedades.

Ronnie y María estaban preocupados porque sus hijos podrían ser mordidos por una de estas enormes ratas. Ellos querían que se exterminaran inmediatamente. Mort estaba de acuerdo. Estos padres preocupados no estaban sobreprotegiendo a sus hijos. Los dientes de las ratas que están constantemente creciendo, causan a las ratas roer cualquier cosa con las que ellas se pongan en contacto, manteniendo sus dientes afilados y listos para su próxima comida. Las ratas contaminan 10 veces más de la cantidad de la comida que ellas se comen, con orina, excrementos, y pelo. Las ratas son portadoras de al menos 10 diferentes tipos de enfermedades incluyendo la plaga bubónica, tifus murine, ictericia contagiosa, leptospirosis, rabia, fiebre por mordedura de rata, e intoxicación alimenticia bacterial. Una mordida de inclusive una rata domesticada puede causar "Fiebre por Mordedura de Ratas", la cual ha sido fatal en 7-10% de los casos. En muchas ocasiones las ratas muerden a los niños mientras tratan de obtener los trozos de comida que no le fueron quitados al niño antes de ir a la cama. Estos padres actuaban por el bien de sus hijos. Mort pensaba acerca de la salud de la anciana que vivía en la casa.

Mort sabía que las ratas son consideradas por la ley un problema sanitario y el Departamento de Salud puede tomar acciones a fin de eliminar el problema. El quería actuar rápido sobre esta urgente materia. El desarrolló un plan de acción. Primero, él enviaría al fotógrafo del Departamento de Salud a tomar fotos de la casa y cerca durante el crepúsculo. Segundo, el prepararía la demanda solicitando el requerimiento judicial de erradicar la infección de roedores.

Al siguiente día, el más habilidoso fotógrafo del Departamento de Salud, Michael Rybolowik, entregó increíbles fotos gráficas de numerosas ratas posadas en el alféizar de la ventana de Mary y en otros sitios de la propiedad. Mientras Mort estudiaba las fotos, él empezó a imaginarse el peor posible escenario: *El portador de citaciones entrega la demanda a Mary. Mientras la anciana mujer le está siendo leída la demanda, sufre de un ataque al corazón y a pesar de los grandes esfuerzos a fin de resucitarla, ella muere del shock. La prensa local es contactada, y Mort es criticado por el impropio manejo del caso y por la muerte de esta maravillosa indefensa abuelita.*

Esta no era un resultado con el que Mort pudiera vivir. El decidió que debía haber una mejor vía. El decidió que antes de introducir la demanda, visitaría a Mary a fin de ver si ella cooperaría y dejaría la casa mientras las ratas eran erradicadas. Mort se aventuró hacia la luz directa del sol, el calor y la humedad a fin de ver si Mary y él podían resolver este problema.

Mientras Mort se acercaba a la casa de Mary, se confrontaba con sus más grandes miedos a las ratas. A pesar de que su mente estaba enfocada en olvidarlo, con cada paso acercándose a la puerta de la casa de Mary, la espeluznante escena Orwelliana de la película, "1984", estaba en constante repetición: El mayor miedo hacia las ratas de un prisionero es explotado exitosamente mientras es torturado en un cuarto lleno de ratas enjauladas. Cada vez que él no cumple con los requerimientos del torturador, las enfadadas alimañas son movidas más cerca y más cerca de su cara. Mort temblaba con el recuerdo mientras tocaba la puerta de la casa de Mary. Al principio no hubo respuesta; Mort estaba listo para irse. Mientras él levantaba su mano para tocar la puerta una segunda vez, sintió que su cuerpo completo quería bajar corriendo la escalera hacia la acera y a la seguridad de la calle. Mort empuñó su mano hacia la pesada puerta de madera. La puerta se abrió lentamente. Delante de él se paró Mary, una anciana mujer extremadamente frágil que le recordó a Mort a su propia abuela. Mort inmediatamente notó que las dos rodillas de Mary estaban envueltas con gasa. El se preguntó si la gasa estaba cubriendo las mordeduras de estos eternos roedores.

Mirando a través de la puerta abierta, Mort vio múltiples ratas correteando en la sala de Mary. En el suelo estaba un sartén lleno de agua para las ratas tomar, un antiguo plato de Coca Cola con pan blanco para las ratas comer. Había excremento de ratas cubriendo cada pulgada del piso y muebles.

Mary invitó a Mort a entrar a su casa. La visión del prisionero torturado 1984 vino otra vez a la mente de Mort. Nada pudo haberlo preparado para lo que pudo ver después. Mientras él miraba al sofá de la sala pudo notar que Mary utilizaba el sofá como cama de dormir, sus almohadas estaban en un extremo del sofá. El estaba disturbado por un aceitoso contorno de la cabeza de Mary que era segregado mientras ella dormía. La mancha de aceite era un "camino de ratas." Las ratas dejan un rastro de aceite en las áreas que ellas frecuentan. Este camino de ratas demostraba que ellas habían puesto su aceitoso cuerpo entre la cabeza de Mary y la pared al lado del sofá.

Mort ahora debía tomar una decisión legal-moral.

La decisión legal, tratar de convencer a Mary de salir voluntariamente de su casa, y si ella no salía voluntariamente, solicitar una orden judicial a fin de sacarla de su nido de ratas (lo cual tomaría al menos ocho horas). O bien ordenarle la salida de su casa sin autoridad legal alguna.

La decisión moral, si Mort esperaba las ocho horas para obtener el requerimiento judicial, y Mary moría por mordeduras de rata, él no podría volver a dormir en paz otra vez.

Mort le ordenó a Mary salir de su casa.

Ella dijo que ella se mudaría a un motel local. Ahora Mort tenía que actuar rápido, encontrar una empresa de control de plagas que mataría las alimañas. Emplear fumigadores, quienes pondrían una carpa sobre la casa y la bombearían toda con insecticida.

Después que la carpa fue removida, los exterminadores llenaron ocho bolsas de Hefty con ratas muertas. Mort calculó que cada bolsa tenía cincuenta ratas. Ergo, cuatrocientas ratas habían estado viviendo con Mary. El olor de 400 ratas muertas en los 90 grados Fahrenheit de temperatura era más de lo que Mort podía tolerar. Su bigote estaba lleno con el apestoso olor. El fue a Burdines (ahora Macy's) y buscó tiras de papeles empapadas de perfumes las cuales mantuvo debajo de su nariz por días a fin de acabar con el olor de las ratas muertas.

Después que la casa estaba libre de ratas, una tropa de Boy Scouts vino y la barrió, fregó, pulió y desechó los desperdicios y la basura que se encontraba en la casa. Luego los Boy Scouts hicieron un esfuerzo extra y pintaron cada cuarto. Mary pudo regresar a su casa una semana después de haberse mudado al motel.

Sin embargo, la historia no termina aquí.

Uno de los Inspectores del Ambiente del Departamento de Salud, Jack Freidan, decidió adoptar a Mary; él la visitaría al menos una vez por semana. Le traería flores, tomaría café con ella, y constantemente aseguraría que las ratas no volvieran. Mary vivió en su casa por otros cinco años. Hasta su muerte, Jack puso al día a Mort sobre la salud y bienestar de Mary.

La pregunta que se le hace más a Mort cuando él relata esta historia es la de ¿porqué no recluiste a Mary en una residencia para la tercera edad? Mort responde, que después de haber inspeccionado las residencias de la tercera edad durante su carrera, él las consideró lugares de último recurso. El le daría a su propia abuela otro chance de vivir en su propia casa, y Mary fue su abuela durante esa caliente, húmeda y abrasadora semana de Agosto de 1985. ☼

Madam Rat La

Translated by Roland Pierre, MSMIS, BBA, CISA.

Se te yon lòt jou lè chalè ak imidite ya te rèd nan mwa Daout 1985. Lè sa a Mort te chita nan biwo ak èkondisyone li epi li tap di tèt li ki jan ke li te genyen chans deske li te endedan biwo li ki te fre. Lè ke li fini gade papye ki di sa li te gen pou li fè nan jounen a, li wè ke li te genyen pou rankont ak yon fanmi nan kominote a ki te genyen tèt yo chage ak pwoblèm lasante osijè de anviwònman kote yo te ap viv la.

Ronnie ak Maria tap pote plent pou vwazin yo Grann Mary ki te gen katreven de zan. Grann Mary tap viv poukont li depi karant an nan yon kay ki antoure ak pye bwa ki bay fwi epi yon kloti ki te fèt ak fil fè.

Ronnie ak Maria prezante tèt yo bay Mort epi byen vit yo montre li foto kloti Grann Mary a. Foto yo san mank te montre kloti ke moun yo te pataje ak grann Mary ak anpil gwo rat Nòvejyen ki te byen nouri, e ki te demi pye long. Nan travay li ak zafè sou sante anviwònman,

Mort te konnen ke rat Nòvejyen yo se rat ki pi komen, ke moun konnen pi byen, epi ki yonn nan pi gwo rat yo. Kalite rat sa viv tout kote moun viv, sitou lavil. An depi di fèt ke rat itil nan rechèch nan lasyans biology, Mort te konnen ke rat sovaj kapab danjere anpil epi tou ke yo reskonsab de se ke anpil maladi simaye.

Ronnie ak Maria te gen tèt yo chaje de se ke gwo papa rat yo te kapab mòde pitit yo. Yo te vle pou ke nou ekstèmine yo tou swit. Mort te dakò. Paran sa yo ki tap bat kò yo pa te egzajere nan bezen pwoteje pitit yo. Dan rat ap grandi tout tan sa ki lakòz ke rat ap ronyen tout bagay ke yo rankontre, se yon fason pou yo kapab kenbe dan yo file ak pare pou prochen manje ki vini sou chemen yo. Rat kontamine ak pipi yo, sekresyon yo ak pwal yo 10 fwa plis manje ke yo kapab manje. Rat pote nan yo o mwens 10 kalite maladi tankou pèst bubonic, typhus murine, lajònis ak spirokèt, leptospirosis (jònis), larage, lafièv ke mòde rat lakòz, anpwozònman manje ak mikwòb. Si yon rat mòde yon moun menm si se rat kay li ye, li kapab lakòz ke moun nan soufri ak maladi lafièv rat mòde "rat bite fever" ki lakòz ke moun nan mouri 7 a 10 fwa sou chak 100 fwa. Anpil fwa rat mòde ti moun lè yo ap chache manje ti kras rès manje ki rete sou ti moun nan lè ke ti moun nan al domi san yo pa fè twalèt li. Paran sa yo tap agi pou byen pitit yo. Mort tap chaje tèt li pou lasante grann moun la ki te abite nan kay la.

Mort te konnen ke dapre atik la lwa rat konsidere kòm yon nwizans pou lasante, ke depatman lasante te kapab prann aksyon pou fè moun nan fè nwizans sa a disparèt. Li te vle agi vit sou zafè sa a ki te mande yon aksyon rapid. Li mete sou pye yon plan pou li pase a laksyon.

Premyèman, li tap voye fotograf depatman lasante a pou li pran foto kay la ak kloti a lè solèy kouche. Deziyèmman, li tap fè papye pou rele mèt kay la nan leta pou fè li retire rat yo.

Jou an apre a fotograf depatman lasante a Michael Ribolowik pote de foto ki byen montre kantite rat ki tap pandye nan rebò fenèt yo ak tout lòt kote nan pwopriete a. Pandan ke Mort ap etidye foto yo li imajine nan tèt li ka ki pi grav la; kote ke yon yisye pote papye tenbre bay Grann Mary. Epi pandan ke yisye a ap li papye tenbre leta a ba li, gran moun nan fè yon arè di kè, epi ke malgre tout efò pou resisite li, li mouri nan chòk. Laprès lokal la vini, epi jounalist yo kritike Mort paske li pa te byen mennen ka sa a, epi tou li touye bon ti grann sa a ki pase tout vi li ap kwit bon ti bonbon.

Mort pa te kapab viv byen ak rezilta sa a. Li deside ke genyen yon mwayen ki pi bon. Avan li fè papye tenbre pou li asiyen gran moun nan nan leta, li tap pral rann vizit kay Grann Mary pou wè si li ta dakò pou li kite kay la pandan ke yo ap ekstèmine rat yo. Lè fè klè, nan mitan chalè ak imidite, Mort prann chans li pou wè si Mary ak li menm takap rezoud pwoblèm la.

Lè Mort ap rive pre kay la, lapè rat la konmanse ap trakase li. Byen ke lespri li te konsantre sou bliye rat yo, chak pa ke li te fè pou li apwoche pòt kay Mary a, yon terib epizòd de yon film sinema ki rele "1984" tap parèt tou tan devan je li. Nan film sinema sa a yo te sèvi ak laperèz de rat ke yon prisonye te genyen pou yo fè li soufri nan yon kalòj plen ak rat. Chak fwa ke prisonye a pa te fè sa bouwo li yo te vle, yo te rapwoche makòn rat enkolè yo pi pre ak figi li a chak fwa. Lè ke li frape pòt Grann Mary a Mort te gen frison paske li tap sonje film sa a. Pa te gen moun ki reponn pòt la okòmansman, Mort te pare pou li ale fè wout li. Lè li tap pral frape pòt la yon dezyèm fwa, li santi ke tout kò li te vle kouri pou ale nan sekirite sou twotwa nan lari a. Mort frape jwenti dwèt li sou pòt an bwa byen lou a. Pòt la ouvri dousman. Devan li te kanpe Mary yon ti gran moun byen frajil epi byen vye ki te fè Mort sonje pwòp grann li. Mort remake tout swit ke tou le de jwenti pye grann moun nan te mare ak twal gaz. Li mande tèt li eske twal gaz sa yo pat kouvri kote ke rat yo te mòde gran moun nan tout tan. Lè li gade an dedan kay la nan pòt ki te ouvri a, li wè pil rat ki tap fè lago nan salon gran moun nan.A tè nan pyès la te genyen yon kaswòl ak dlo pou rat yo te bwè epi sou yon ansyen plato koka kola te genyen pen blan pou rat yo manje. Kakarat te kouvri tout a tè a ak tout mèb yo.

Mary te envite Mort en dedan kay la. Lide de film sinema1984 la ak prisonye bouwo tap matirize ak rat yo vini nan tèt Mort ankò. Pa te gen anyen ki te prepare li pou sa li pral wè a. Pandan ke li ap gade yon divan nan salon a, li remake ke Mary te sèvi ak li kòm kabann li. Zòreye li yo te nan yon bout divan a. Genyen yon fòm ki te plen grès kote Mary te mete tèt li lè ke li te ap dòmi. Sa te trakase Mort anpil, paske mak grès la se te yon chemen rat. Rat kite mak grès kote yo pase anpil. Chemen rat la te montre ke rat yo te mete kò yo plen grès ant tèt Mary ak panno mi ki te pre divan a.

Mort te genyen pou li pran yon desizyon la lwa,ak yon desizyon konsyans li

Desizyon la lwa a se te pou fè Mary aksepte kite kay la san yo pa fòse li, epi si li pa vle kite kay la, se te pou yo te prann yon papye tenbre nan lajistis pou fè li soti nan nich rat la (Sa tap prann ywit è de tan pou papye leta fè Mary sòti) Oswa fè li kite kay la san ke leta pa mete bouch nan sa a.

Desizyon konsyans li a se te ke si Mort te tan ywit è de tan epi Mary te mouri anba mòde rat yo li patap kab janm domi an pè nan vi li ankò.

Mort bay Mary lòd pou soti kite kay li.

Mary di ke li tap ale nan yon motèl nan zòn la. Kounye a Mort te dwe agi vit epi jwenn yon konpanyi ki touye bèt pou ekstèmine rat yo. Konpanyi yo anplwaye a te mete yon tant sou kay la epi li te pompe pwazon rat anba tant la pou touye vèmin yo.

Lè yo retire tant la konpanyi ki te ekstèmine bèt yo retire ywit sak Hefty (sak plastik yo sèvi pou mete gwo fatra) plen ak rat. Mort kalkile ke chak sak Hefty yo te genyen (50) senkant rat. Sa vle di kat san rat tap viv ak Mary.

Sant kat san rat mouri nan gwo chalè katrevendis degree Fahrenheit se te plis ke Mort te kapab sipòte. Tout moustach li te plen ak move zodè a. Li ale nan magazen Burdines (ki Macys kounye a) li achte moso papye ki tranpe nan pafen yo ke li kenbe anba nen li pandan anpil jou pou retire odè rat mouri a. Kounye a ke kay la pa te genyen rat ankò gen yon twoup tigason eskout ki vini bale, siye, pase twal mouye, jete tout fatra ki te nan kay la. Epi apre tigason eskout yo fè plis toujou, yo pentire tout pyès kay la. Mary te kapab retounen lakay li yon semen apre ke li te ale nan motèl la. Men istwa a pa fini la. Yon nan enspektè pou lasante anviwònman ki rele Jack Freidman deside pou li adopte Mary, li vizite li omwens yon fwa pa semenn, pote flè pou li, bwè kafe ak li epi asire li ke rat yo pat tounen. Apre sa a, Mary te viv nan kay la pandan kat lane. Jiska se ke Mary mouri, Mort te resevwa nouvèl lasante ak sekirite Mary ke Jack te pote ba li.

Keksyon ke yo mande Mort souvan lè li rakonte istwa sa a se: pouki sa ou pa te fè yo mete Mary nan yon mezon de retrèt pou gran moun (nursing home)? Mort reponn ke li te fè travay enspektè nan mezon retrèt yo epi donk li kwè ke moun dwe ale nan kote sa yo sèlman lè ke yo paka fè otreman. Si se te grann Mort li tap ba li yon chans pou kite li viv nan pwòp kay li, ki donk Mary te vini grann li nan jou gwo chalè ak imidite nan semen mwa Daout 1985 la. ✺

The Best-Laid Plans

"The best laid schemes o' mice an' men/gang aft a-gley"
– To a Mouse by Robert Burns.

By Morton Laitner

A long time ago, 1986 to be specific, I learned a life lesson. Here it is: no matter how carefully a project is planned, something will go wrong.

It was a cold December morning, at 9:00 a.m. as we met on the tenth floor of the old courthouse. I, Mort, the Health Department attorney with a team of expert environmental specialists, Wally Livingstone, Dick Strait and Mike Rybolowik, were preparing for our big day in court. We were fighting a slum-lord by seeking an injunction to have him either repair and clean up his building or have it shut down. Mr. Slum-Lord owned a forty-unit apartment complex in downtown Miami. He was a skinny hallow-faced sixty year old and looked like he didn't care how his tenants lived as long as he got his rent money. Mr. Slum-Lord's poverty-stricken tenants were living in a building with piles of rubbish throughout the complex, which of course lead to a mouse problem.

Wally, the head of the Environmental Health Unit, was prepared to testify that mice can be harmful pests spreading diseases through their parasites and feces. Wally would testify that mice carry and cause the following diseases: rickettsial pox, rat bite fever, food poisoning (namely salmonellosis which is spread to people when food is contaminated by saliva, urine or feces from the mouse). Mice can spread parasites to people such as trichinosis and tapeworm. We not only had photographs taken by Mike Rybolowik of the mouse infestation, but also Dick Strait had caught a live mouse, caged it, and named it Stuart Little. Mort excitedly said, "This would be the best demonstrative evidence to convince the judge to rule in our favor." And after introducing Stuart Little into evidence, the Clerk would have an interesting time keeping Stuart alive.

Mort knew that his witnesses were well prepared for the 9:30 a.m. hearing. While we waited in the Judge's chambers for the trial to commence, we admired Stuart Little in his make-shift home. Little did we know that Stuart was laying his own plans.

The Health Department hadn't bought a professionally-made hamster or gerbil cage or purchased a small aquarium with a mesh top. But, instead, we made our own sturdy-looking wire-mesh cage with removable top. We were all admiring our cute little three-inch common house mouse, when the cage fell out of Wally's hands; the lid flipped open and Stuart Little made a mad dash for freedom.

We scurried around the Judge's chambers trying to look inconspicuous while attempting to find and catch Stuart. Sadly to say for us, Stuart had escaped. Mort then whispered to Wally, Dick and Mike to get the mouse cage out of the courthouse and not mention what happened that fateful morning.

We won the case. Mr. Slum-lord fixed up the apartment complex and eliminated the mouse problem.

As Mort enters the old courthouse twenty-one years later, he wonders if any Stuart Little's relatives are still living on the tenth floor. He smiles and remembers the life lesson: the best laid plans of men, (not always mice), often go awry. ⛅

Los Proyectos Mejores Planeados

Translation by Ninfa Urdaneta

Mucho tiempo atrás, en 1986 para ser específico, aprendí una gran lección. La lección es: no importa lo cuidadosamente que un proyecto es planeado, algo va a salir mal.

Era una mañana fría de Diciembre, a las 9:00 a.m., cuando nos reunimos en el décimo piso del viejo edificio de tribunales. Yo, Mort, el abogado del Departamento de Salud, con un grupo de expertos especialistas ambientales, Wally Livingstone, Dick Strait y Mike Rybolowick, nos preparábamos para el gran día en la Corte. Nosotros estábamos pidiendo un requerimiento judicial en contra del dueño de un edificio de barrio pobre que extorsionaba a sus arrendatarios. El requerimiento tenía por objeto que el propietario reparara y limpiara su edificio o lo clausurara. El propietario era dueño de un edificio que tenía cuarenta apartamentos en el centro de Miami. El era un flaco de cara inexpresiva de sesenta años de edad y parecía como que a él no le importaba como sus inquilinos vivían siempre que él recibiera el dinero de la renta. Los pobres inquilinos de este propietario extorsionador estaban viviendo en un edificio con pilas de residuos domésticos a través del complejo, lo cual por su puesto conducía a un problema de roedores.

Wally, el jefe de la Unidad de Salud Ambiental, estaba preparado para testificar que los ratones pueden ser perjudiciales plagas transmisoras de enfermedades a través de sus parásitos y excrementos. Wally testificaría que los ratones portan y causan las siguientes enfermedades: rickettsiosis pustulosa o vesicular, fiebre por mordedura de ratas, intoxicación alimenticia bacterial (a saber, infección por salmonela, la cual es transmitida a las personas cuando la comida es contaminada con la saliva, orina o excremento de roedores). Los ratones pueden transmitir parásitos a las personas tales como trichinosis y solitaria. Nosotros no solo teníamos fotografías tomadas por Mike Rybolowik, sino que también Dick Strait había atrapado un ratón vivo, lo enjauló, y lo llamó Stuart Little. Mort emocionado dijo, "Esta sería la mejor evidencia demostrativa para convencer al Juez a dictaminar en nuestro favor." Y después de introducir a Stuart Little como evidencia, el Oficial del Juzgado tendría un rato interesante manteniendo a Stuart vivo.

Mort sabía que sus testigos estaban bien preparados para la audiencia de las 9:30 a.m. Mientras esperábamos en la cámara del Juez para comenzar el juicio, nosotros admirábamos a Stuart Little en su casa temporal. Poco sabíamos que Stuart estaba tramando sus propios planes.

El Departamento de Salud no había comprado una jaula especialmente hecha para un roedor pequeño o hámster ni comprado un acuario pequeño con una malla arriba. Por el contrario, nosotros hicimos nuestra propia jaula de alambre aparentemente resistente con la parte superior removible. Todos estábamos admirando nuestro lindo y ordinario ratoncito de casa de tres pulgadas, cuando la caja se le cayó de las manos a Wally; la tapa se abrió y Stuart Little corrió desenfrenadamente hacia su libertad.

Nosotros corrimos discretamente por toda la cámara del Juez tratando de encontrar y atrapar a Stuart. Desafortunadamente para nosotros, Stuart se había escapado. Mort les indicó en voz baja a Wally, Dick y Mike que sacaran la jaula del ratón fuera del recinto de la corte y no mencionaran lo que pasó esa fatídica mañana.

Nosotros ganamos el caso. El arrendador arregló el complejo de apartamentos y eliminó el problema de roedores.

Cuando Mort entra al viejo edificio de tribunales veintiún años después, el se pregunta si alguno de los parientes de Stuart Little están todavía viviendo en el décimo piso. Se sonríe y recuerda la gran lección: los proyectos mejores planeados de los hombre, (no siempre de los ratones), con frecuencia fallan.

Pi Bon Plan Ke Yon Moun Kapab Pare

Translated by Roland Pierre, MSMIS, BBA, CISA.

Depi tan lontan, nan lane 1986 mwen te aprann yon leson lavi. Men leson a: Menm si ou pran tout kalite prekosyon pou ou byen planifye yon pwojè gen yon bagay ki ka mal pase kan menm. Se te yon mwa Desanm ki te fè fredi, li te nevè di maten lè nou te rankontre nan diziyèm etaj ansyen tribinal lajistis la. Mwen menm Mort, avoka depatman sante piblik ak yon ekip espesyalist nan lasante anviwònman Wally Livingstone, Dick Strait, ak Mike Rybolowik, nou tap pare pou yon gwo jou nan tribinal lajistis la.

Nou te ap fè yon pwose ak yon move pwopriyetè pou te fè leta fose li repare bilding li a oswa detwi li. Move pwopriyetè sa a te genyen yon bilding ak karant apatman nan anba lavil Miami. Se te yon misye swasant lane ki te mens ak yon figi rale, eki pa te bezwen konnen ki jan lokatè li yo te ap viv, yon sèl bagay ki te enterese li se te ranmase lajan lwaye li. Malere lokatè yo te ap viv nan yon bilding ak fatra tout kote sa ki te lakòz ke te genyen pwoblèm ak vèmin sourit.

Wally ki te chèf sèvis anviwònman lasante te pare pou li temwanye ke sourit se yon bèt danjere ki kapab simaye maladi ak matyè fekal yo epi ak ti bèt parazit ki sou kò yo. Willy ta prale temwanye ke sourit bay maladi sa yo rele rickettsial pox, lafièv ke mòde rat lakòz, anpwazonman manje (sitou mikwòb salmonela ki gaye lè manje moun manje enfekte ak krache, pipi, ak matyè fekal sourit yo. Sourit kapab gaye ka moun bèt parazit tankou vè trichinosis, epi vè yo rele

Oxyur la. Nou te genyen foto ke Mike Rybolowik te pran de sourit yo, men tou Dick Strait te trape yon sourit, te mete li nan yon kalòj epi rele li Stuart Little (non yon ti sourit ke yon fanmi te adopte nan yon film sinema) Mort ki te tou eksite di ke: se pral pi bon prèv pou al montre jij la pou fè nou genyen kòz la. Apre ke nou montre Stuart Little kòm prèv, grefye a te pase yon moman enteresan ap eseye kenbe Stuart vivan.

Mort te konnen ke temwen li yo te byen pare pou pwose a ki te pou kòmanse a nevè edmi. Pandan nou te ap tann nan chamb jij la pou pwosè a kòmanse nou te ap fè bèl konpliman pou Stuart Little ki te nan ti kay ke nou te fè pou li a. Depatman lasante pa te achte yon kalòj ke yon gwo bòs te fè pou yon kochonden, oswa yon ti bwat an vit ak yon filè sou li. Men okontrè nou te fè yon kalòj an grillaj an fè ak yon tèt ke nou te kapab retire. Nou te ap fè bèl konpliman pou bèl ti sourit ki mezire twa pous e ke moun jwenn tout kote, lè ke kalòj la ke Wally te kenbe sòt tonbe, kouvèti a soti, epi Stuart Little sove. Nou tout te ap monte desann nan chamb jij la ap eseye trape Stuart san ke moun pa konnen sa nou tap fè. Malerèzman pou nou Stuart te sove. Mort lè sa a, tou ba di Wally, Dick ak Mike pou retire kalòj sourit la nan tribinal la byen vit epi pa janm di kisa ki te pase nan maten move jou sila a. Nou genyen pwose a, move pwopriyetè a repare bilding ak apatman yo epi pwoblèm sourit la tou fini pou lokatè yo.

Lè Mort ap antre tribinal la venteen (21) lane apre li ap mande tèt li eske kèk fanmi Stuart Little dwe abite toujou nan dizyèm etaj tribinal la. Li ri epi li sonje leson lavi sa a; pi bon kalite plan ke moun (pa toujou sourit) pare kapab mal pase kan menm. ☀

The Big Stick[5]

By Morton Laitner

It was spring 2003 and SARS[6] was quickly making its journey around the globe. The world watched as this scary disease killed 744 people. With over eight thousand people sick, no one knew which country would be affected next. Americans grew more frightened when our northern Canadian neighbors began dying.

All told, forty-three Canadians died of SARS. Toronto was quarantining its citizenry. The Miami-Dade County Health Department's Epidemiology staff, under the august direction of Chief Physician Fermin Leguen, was anxiously awaiting the first case of SARS to hit America.

Was SARS destined to be our modern-day plague?

Our stomachs dropped as we received notice from the Centers for Disease Control that Miami had a viable SARS threat. An Orthodox

5 Big Stick Diplomacy or Big Stick Policy was the slogan describing U.S. President Theodore Roosevelt's corollary to the Monroe Doctrine. The United States, he claimed, had the right not only to oppose European intervention in the Western Hemisphere, but also to intervene itself in the domestic affairs of its neighbors if they proved unable to maintain order and national sovereignty on their own. http://en.wikipedia.org/wiki/Big_stick_diplomacy
6 SARS is the acronym for Severe Acute Respiratory Syndrome.

Rabbi, working as a jeweler, had recently returned from a business trip to: China, Hong Kong, Taiwan and the Province of Ontario, Canada. These nations had the highest rate of SARS cases in the world. The Rabbi was now ill with many SARS symptoms: fever, cough, sore throat, and gastrointestinal problems. He lived alone at his home on Miami Beach. His social life revolved mainly around his religion and daily trips to the Synagogue.

His humble temple was located four short blocks from his home. Despite his ailments, the Rabbi continued his daily devotional journey to pray with approximately twenty fellow congregants.

Dr. Leguen warned the clergyman that his daily journey to the Temple could spread this deadly disease to the whole community and most affect the Synagogue members. The Rabbi did not heed the good doctor's warning.

Michael Greif, a Tallahassee Health Department Attorney with an expertise in SARS, requested that Mort Laitner's and Judy Elfont, the local health lawyers intercede to convince the Rabbi to stay at home. Mort and Judy called the Rabbi and explained about the transmission of SARS and the high mortality rate. The Rabbi had done a lot of reading about SARS during his lengthy trip around the world, and politely requested that he speak with another medical doctor about his condition. The Rabbi, in classic Talmudic style, questioned why he was getting medical advice from attorneys. Mort realized he would have to bring in the state's Division Director for Disease Control, Dr. Landis Crockett.

Dr. Crockett had the credentials that would impress the religious leader. He had a medical degree from an Ivy League school and a Masters in Public Health from John Hopkins. Although Mort hoped the Rabbi would listen to Dr. Crockett, he wanted a back-up plan.

An avid history buff, Mort thought about former president Theodore Roosevelt's famous quote which came from a West African proverb,

"Speak softly and carry a big stick, and you will go far."

Mort knew in order to protect the community he would need to have more than just a soft speech from a highly qualified doctor. He would need to carry a big stick as well. It is not without great thought that the Health Department undertakes measures to quarantine individuals against their will. However, in a case such as this, the involuntary quarantine stick was the only one that would wield enough strength to keep the Rabbi from infecting the city with SARS.

Mort didn't want to go as far as to meet the Rabbi in person. However, he gathered his N-95 masks, his anti-bacterial hand gel and a quarantine order. His plan, should the doctor's conversation with the Rabbi fail, was to visit the Rabbi's home with the police.

Dr. Crockett, Michael, Judy and Mort managed to get the Rabbi on the phone. The doctor did an admiral job of explaining the risk of exposure to the community, the epidemiology of the disease and how extremely important it was for the Rabbi to stay and to pray at home until his period of communicability was over.

Then Mort added in a soft voice, "Rabbi, if it is determined that you have gone back to the Temple after this verbal warning we will immediately place you under home quarantine and surround your home with yellow police crime scene tape and around-the-clock police surveillance until you are no longer considered a threat."

Finally, the Rabbi understood. He followed the Health Department's orders and prayed alone at his home. Alone in his office, Mort also prayed. His prayer dealt with thanks for not having to risk his life, to President Teddy Roosevelt and to the wise West African proverb writer. ☀

Habla Suave y ten Mano Dura, y Llegarás Lejos

Translated by Ninfa Urdaneta

Era la primavera del 2003 y el SARS estaba rápidamente viajando por todo el planeta. El mundo presenció como esta espeluznante enfermedad mató 744 personas. Con más de ocho mil personas enfermas, nadie sabía cual sería el siguiente país afectado. Los americanos se asustaron todavía más cuando nuestros vecinos Canadienses del Norte se empezaron a morir.

En total, cuarenta y tres Canadienses murieron por causa del SARS. Toronto estaba poniendo en cuarentena a sus ciudadanos. El equipo de Epidemiología del Departamento de Salud del Condado de Miami-Dade, bajo la honorable dirección de su Médico Principal Fermin Leguen, estaba ansiosamente esperando que el primer caso de SARS apareciera en los Estados Unidos de Norte América.

¿Estaba el SARS destinado a ser la plaga moderna de nuestros días?

Nuestros estómagos se exaltaron cuando recibimos la noticia del Cetro de Control de Enfermedades (Centers for Disease Control) de que Miami tenía una viable amenaza de SARS. Un Rabino ortodoxo, quien trabajaba como joyero, había recientemente regresado de un viaje de negocio de China, Hong Kong, Taiwán y de la Provincia de Ontario, Canadá. Estas naciones tenían el índice más alto de casos de SARS en el mundo. El Rabino estaba enfermo con muchos síntomas del SARS: fiebre, tos, dolor de garganta, y problemas gastrointestinales. El vivía solo en su casa en Miami Beach. Su vida social giraba mayormente alrededor de su religión y sus viajes diarios a la Sinagoga.

Su humilde templo estaba localizado a cuatro cuadras cortas de su casa. A pesar de su enfermedad, el Rabino continuó con devoción sus viajes diarios a rezar con aproximadamente veinte compañeros de congregación.

Dr. Leguen le advirtió al clérigo que sus viajes diarios al Templo podían propagar la mortífera enfermedad a toda la comunidad y sobretodo a los miembros de la Sinagoga. El Rabino no hizo caso a las buenas advertencias del doctor.

Michael Greif, un abogado con experticia en SARS del Departamento de Salud en Tallahassee, pidió que Mort Laitner y Judy Elfont, los abogados locales del Departamento de Salud, intercedieran a fin de convencer al Rabino que se quedara en su casa. Mort y Judy llamaron al Rabino y le explicaron acerca de la transmisión del SARS y el alto índice de mortalidad. El Rabino había leído bastante acerca del SARS durante su largo viaje alrededor del mundo, y educadamente pidió hablar con otro doctor sobre su condición. El Rabino, en estilo clásico Talmúdico, cuestionó por qué él estaba recibiendo consejos médicos de abogados. Mort se dio cuenta que él tenía que involucrar al Director de la División de Control de Enfermedades del Estado, Dr. Landis Crockett.

El Dr. Crockett tenía las credenciales que impresionarían al líder religioso. Se había graduado de médico en una de las Universidades de la Ivy League y tenía un Master en Salud Pública de la Universidad de John Hopkins. Aunque Mort esperaba que el Rabino oyera a Dr. Crockett, él tenía que tener un segundo plan.

Un ávido aficionado de la historia, Mort pensó acerca de la famosa cita del ex-presidente Theodoro Roosevelt, la cual vino de un proverbio de África Occidental.

"Speak softly and carry a big stick and you will go far."
(Habla suave y ten mano dura, y llegarás lejos)

Mort sabía que a fin de proteger la comunidad él tenía que tener algo más que un lenguaje suave de un doctor altamente calificado. El tenía que tener mano dura también. Es después de meditarlo bien que el Departamento de Salud toma las medidas a fin de poner en cuarentena a individuos contra su voluntad. Sin embargo, en un caso como este la cuarentena involuntaria era lo único que podía ejercer suficiente fuerza para prevenir que el Rabino infectara la ciudad con SARS.

Mort no quería llegar a reunirse en persona con el Rabino. Sin embargo, juntó sus máscaras N-95, su gel de mano antibacterial y la orden de poner en cuarentena. Su plan, si la conversación del doctor con el Rabino fallaba, era la de visitar la casa del Rabino con la policía.

Dr. Crockett, Michael, Judy y Mort lograron comunicarse con el Rabino por teléfono. El doctor hizo un admirable trabajo al explicar los riesgos de exponer a la comunidad, la epidemiología de la enfermedad y lo importante que era que el Rabino se quedara y rezara en su casa hasta que el periodo infeccioso de la enfermedad terminara.

Luego Mort añadió en tono suave, "Rabino, si es determinado que usted ha ido de nuevo al Templo después de esta advertencia verbal procederemos inmediatamente a ponerlo en cuarentena y rodearemos su casa con cinta amarilla de escena de crimen de la policía y pondremos vigilancia policial continuada, día y noche, hasta que usted no sea considerado un amenaza."

Finalmente, el Rabino entendió. El siguió las órdenes del Departamento de Salud y rezó solo en su casa. Solo en su oficina, Mort también rezó. Sus oraciones eran para dar las gracias por no haber tenido que poner en riesgo su vida, al Presidente Teddy Roosevelt y al sabio proverbio de África Occidental. ☼

Pale Dousman Epi Mache Ak Yon Bwa Long Epi Ou Va Ale Lwen

Creole translation by : Roland R. Pierre, MSMIS, BBA, CISA.

Se te nan prentan 2003 lè maladi SARS te ap fè chemen li sou latè. Tout moun sou latè tap gade kijan ke maladi ki bay laperèz la te touye 744 moun. Ak plis ke ywit mil moun malad ak SARS pa genyen moun ki te konnen nan ki peyi maladi a tap ale apre. Moun Ozetazini Damerik te ap gen laperèz plis chak jou lè ke vwazen yo nan pati Nò Kanada te kòmanse mouri.

Ototal karannt twa Kanadyen te mouri ak SARS. Toronto te ap mete moun pwovens la an karanntèn. Anplwaye sèvis epidem- depatman sante piblik nan Miyami sou zòd doktè an chèf Fermer Leguen tap tann ak kè sere ki te premye ka SARS ki tap parèt nan peyi Lèzetazini.

Eske SARS tap vin tounen lapèst tan modèn yo?

Lestomak nou te chavire lè ke CDC, Sant pou Kontwòl Maladi, te di nou ke Miyami te menase ak danje SARS. Yon Orthodox Rabbi (yon chèf legliz jwif yo) ki te fè travay ofèv tou, te fèk tounen soti nan peyi Lachin, Hongkong, Taiwan ak pwovens Ontario nan Kanada kote ke li te ale pou biznis li. Peyi kote misye Rabbi sa a te ale yo te genyen plis ka SARS ke nan tout lòt peyi sou latè. Misye Rabbi a te malad ak anpil sentòm maladi SARS tankou: lafièv, tous, doulè nan gòj, ak pwoblem nan entesten li ak lestomak li. Li te ap viv poukont li nan kay li nan Miyami Beach. Lavi li se te sitou ale nan aktivite relijyon li epi sitou ale chak jou nan legliz li (sinagòg).

Legliz sinagòg li a pa te yon gwo legliz epi li te sèlman kat blòk de lakay li. Malgre ke li te malad Rabbi a te kontinye ale nan legliz li chak jou kote ke li te lapryè ak a pe prè ven manb legliz la.

Doktè Leguen bay rabbi a avètisman ke ale nan legliz sinagòg la chak jou jan ke li tap fè a tap lakòz ke maladi ki ap touye moun sa a ta va gaye nan kominote a, sitou nan mitan manb legliz li a. Rabbi a pate swiv bon konsèy doktè a. Avoka depatman sante piblik nan Talaasi (Tallahassee) Michael Greif yon avoka ki te genyen eksperians nan SARS, mande ke Mort Laitner ak Judy Elfont avoka depatman sante piblik nan Miyami yo al pale ak Rabbi a pou yo fè li konprann ke se pou li te sèt oblije rete lakay li.

Mort ak Judy rele Rabbi a epi yo eksplike li ki jan maladi SARS la gaye ak pil kantite moun malad ki te déjà mouri anba maladi a. Rabbi a te li anpil sou maladi SARS la pandan vwayaj byen long li te fè nan peyi sou latè a. Ak bon jan mannyè Rabbi a mande pale ak yon doktè osijè de maladi li a. Rabbi a te apiye li sou liv la lwa jwif pou li mande pou ki sa ke se avoka olye de doktè ki te ap ba li konsèy lasante. Mort te rann li kont ke se pou li te mande doktè Landis Crockett, direktè divizyon kontwòl maladi pou Leta Florid la, pou pale ak Rabbi a. Doktè Crockett se yon maton, yon otorite nan koze kontwòl maladi ki te kapab fè Rabbi a rete bouch be. Doktè a te genyen diplòm ke li te etidye nan pi gwo inivèsite nan peyi Ameriken epi tou li te genyen yon diplòm mastè nan zafè sante piblik ki soti nan yon gwo inivèsite nan peyi a ki rele John Hopkins. Menm si Mort te espere ke Rabbi a tap koute doktè Crockett li te vle yon lòt plan pou si sa pat mache.

Mort se yon moun ki konnen istwa peyi li byen, li sonje pawòl prezidan Theodore Roosevelt ki soti de yon pwovèb nan Lwès peyi Lafrik:

"Pale dousman epi mache ak yon bwa long epi ou va rive lwen."

Mort te konnen ke si pou li te pwoteje kominote a li tap bezwen plis ke bèl pawòl yon doktè ki te byen save. Li konnen ke se pou li te mache ak yon bwa long tou. Se apre ke yo reflechi anpil ke depatman lasante konn prann desizyon pou yo fòse yon moun nan karantèn kont volonte li. Men nan yon ka konsa bwa long pou fose moun nan karantèn, se te sèl mwayen pou anpeche Rabbi a enfekte tout lavil la ak maladi SARS la.

Mort pa te vle fè bagay yo ale si tèlman lwen ke li tap oblije al rankontre ak Rabbi a pou ke kat je kontre. Men an tou ka li te pare kò li pou si oka li tap sèt oblije al rankontre ak Rabbi a. Li prann mask N-95 pou figi li, gèl pou touye mikwòb sou men li, epi yon papye tenbre leta pou mete moun nan karantèn. Plan Mort se pou li te vizite kay Rabbi ak lapolis si konvèsasyon doktè a ak Rabbi a pate fè Rabbi a chanje lide li.

Doktè Crokett, Michael, Judy ak Mort rele nan telefòn jouk Rabbi a prann telefòn la. Doktè a te fè yon travay ekstraodinè nan jan li eksplike Rabbi a danje pou gaye maladi a nan kominote a, ki kote, ak ki jan maladi a gaye, epi sitou enpòtans pou li rete lapryè lakay li jouktan li pakab pase maladi a bay lòt moun ankò.

Epi Mort ajoute ak yon vwa dous : "Rabbi apre avètisman sa a si nou jwenn ke ou ale nan legliz sinagòg la ankò nap mete ou nan karantèn lakay ou epi nou ap ansèkle kay ou ak tep jòn lapolis sèvi kote gen yon krim ki fèt, epi tou nou ap mete lapolis veye ou lajounen kou lannwit jiska se ke ou pa yon danje ankò pou lòt moun".

Alafen Rabbi a konprann. Li swiv lòd depatman sante piblik la, li lapryè pou kont li la kay li. Poukont li tou nan biwo li Mort te lapryè tou. Li te lapryè pou remèsye prezidan Teddy Roosevelt ak moun saj nan peyi nan Lwès Lafrik de se ke yo te ede li pou li pa te oblije ale bòkote moun malad la epi pran gwo chans ak lavi li. ☼

Tears for Fears[7]

Written by Lori S. Jordahl MBA – HA

ori, a health department employee, who had seen only 21 summers, was learning what it was like to work in the world of AIDS in the mid 1980's. In those early AIDS years, daily calls and visits from ordinary people were filled with panic, hysteria, anger, loss, and sadness.

Ring...Ring...

"Good morning. Lori here."

"I heard that the person in my apartment complex has AIDS. Please investigate so I can get out of my lease."

Ring...Ring...

"Good afternoon. Can I help you?"

"Make the manager put in a separate washer and dryer for people with AIDS."

Ring...Ring...

"Good evening. What is your question?"

"If I stuff a whole bunch of tissues in my date's mouth and there is no blood, is it safe to kiss?"

Ring...Ring...

"Good morning. You want us to do what!?!"

7 Tears for Fears era una popular banda de pop formada a principio de los años 1980. Tears for Fears ha vendido más de 21 millones de copias a nivel mundial. El nombre de la banda es derivado del tratamiento de psicoterapia primal que lleva el mismo nombre desarrollada por Arthur Janov, la cual se hizo famosa después que John Lennon se hizo paciente de Janov. Mientras se somete a la psicoterapia primal, el paciente es fomentado a "re-experimentar" sus primeros, estados emocionales dramáticos (aún los perinatales), incluyendo el gritar como un bebé, de ahí la expresión "tears for fears." (Wikipedia, http://www.wikipedia.org/.

"Empty and clean all public pools and put signs up that people with AIDS can't swim."

Ring...Ring...
"Good afternoon. Can I help you?"
"Can you make my boyfriend get tested and give me the results?"

Ring...Ring...
"Good evening. You want what?"
"Inspect and test doctors, teachers, restaurant workers, nail stylists, then post their results for everyone to see."

Ring...Ring...
"Good morning. You want to bring what?"
"I want to bring someone's blood samples on tissues and razors to be tested."

Ring...Ring...
"Good evening. You want us to do what?"
"Can't you quarantine everyone who tests positive?"

Lori and the AIDS team felt totally overwhelmed. They wanted to scream.

"Shout, shout.
Let it all out.
These are the things I can do without.
Come on.
I'm talking to you.
Come on."

They were like infants in the fetal position expressing their tears for fears.

Every day, the team was giving 10 or more positive results which would tear up even their toughest counselor. Next, they had to explain the lack of treatment available.

Lori had to explain "the facts" or "give results" to people in denial who literally put their fingers in their ears.

The team bargained with patients to adopt safer sex practices.

Some listened. Some did not. At-risk patients who received negative test results thinking they were lucky and immune would often find out the next time their luck had run out.

Even some of Lori's co-workers were diagnosed with AIDS.

The most challenging aspect of this time was trying to be patient with the ignorance and prejudice.

How did Lori and the team survive this flood of ignorance and prejudice?

THROUGH PASSIONATE PUBLIC HEALTH! ☼

Lágrimas por Miedos[8]

Escrito por Lori S. Jordahl MBA – HA
Editado por Mort Laitner, Heather Beaton,
Ninfa Urdaneta y Frederick Villari.

Lori, una empleada del Departamento de Salud, quien había vivido solo 21 primaveras, estaba aprendiendo como era trabajar en el mundo del SIDA a mediados de los años '80. En aquellos primeros años del SIDA, llamadas y visitas diarias de personas ordinarias estaban llenas de pánico, histeria, ira, pérdida, y tristeza.

Ring...Ring...
"Buenos Días, es Lori."
"Yo oí que una persona en mi complejo apartamentos tiene SIDA. Por favor, investiguen a fin de yo poderme salir de mi contrato de alquiler."

Ring...Ring...
"Buenas tardes, ¿Puedo ayudarle?"
"Obliguen al manager a poner una lavadora y secadora separadas para la gente con SIDA."

8 Tears for Fears era una popular banda de pop formada a principio de los años 1980. Tears for Fears ha vendido más de 21 millones de copias a nivel mundial. El nombre de la banda es derivado del tratamiento de psicoterapia primal que lleva el mismo nombre desarrollada por Arthur Janov, la cual se hizo famosa después que John Lennon se hizo paciente de Janov. Mientras se somete a la psicoterapia primal, el paciente es fomentado a "re-experimentar" sus primeros, estados emocionales dramáticos (aún los perinatales), incluyendo el gritar como un bebé, de ahí la expresión "tears for fears." Wikipedia, http://www.wikipedia.org/.

Ring...Ring...
"Buenas noches, ¿Cuál es su pregunta?"
"¿Si yo relleno con un montón de kleenex la boca de la persona con la que tengo una cita y no hay sangre, estaré fuera de peligro al besarle?"

Ring...Ring...
"Buenos días, ¡¿Usted quiere que nosotros hagamos qué?!"
"Vacíen y limpien todas las piscinas públicas y pongan letreros indicando que personas con SIDA no pueden bañarse."

Ring...Ring...
"Buenas tardes, ¿Le puedo ayudar?"
"¿Pueden hacer que mi novio se haga la prueba y me dan a mi los resultados?"

Ring...Ring...
"Buenas noches, ¿Usted quiere qué?"
"Examinen y háganle pruebas a los doctores,maestros, trabajadores en restaurantes, manicuristas, luego exhiban los resultados a fin de que todo el mundo los pueda ver."

Ring...Ring...
"Buenos días, ¿Usted quiere traer qué?"
"Yo quiero llevar muestras de sangre en kleenex y afeitadoras a fin de que las examinen."

Ring...Ring...
"Buenas noches, ¿Usted quiere que nosotros hagamos qué?"
"¿No pueden poner a todo el que resulte positivo en cuarentena?"

Lori y el equipo de SIDA se sentían totalmente abrumados. Ellos querían gritar:

"Shout, shout.
Let it all out.
These are the things I can do without.
Come on.
I am talking to you.

Come on."[9]

"Grita, grita.
Exprésalo todo.
Estas son las cosas que yo no necesito.
Vamos.
Te estoy hablando a ti.
Vamos."

Ellos estaban como bebés en la posición fetal expresando sus lágrimas por miedos.

Todos los días, el equipo estaba dando 10 o más resultados positivos, los cuales podrían romper en pedazos al más fuerte de los consejeros. Después, ellos tenían que explicar la falta de tratamiento disponible.

Lori tenía que explicar "los hechos" o "dar resultados" a personas en denegación quienes literalmente se tapaban los oídos.

El equipo acordó con sus pacientes la adopción de prácticas sexuales más seguras. Algunos prestaron atención. Otros no. Los pacientes en riesgo que recibieron resultados negativos, pensando que ellos tenían suerte y eran inmunes a menudo se enteraban la siguiente vez de que su suerte se había terminado.

Inclusive algunos de los compañeros de trabajo de Lori fueron diagnosticados con SIDA.

El mayor reto de estos tiempos fue el tratar de ser paciente con la ignorancia y el prejuicio.

¿Cómo Lori y el equipo sobrevivieron esta inundación de ignorancia y prejuicio?

¡A TRAVES DE LA PASION POR LA SALUD PUBLICA! ☼

9 Extracto de Shout, por Tears for Fears.

Moun Tap Krye Paske Yo Te Gen Laperèz Nan Kò Yo

Se Lori Jordahl MBA-HA ki ekri istwa sa a
Moun ki korije istwa pou piblye li se: Mort Laitner, Heather Beaton,
Ninfa Urdaneta, Fredrick Villari.

Lori se yon anplwaye depatman lasante ki te wè sèlman 21 sezon chalè (te genyen sèlman 21 lane) tap pral fè konesans ak sa sa vle di pou travay nan zafè Sida otou lane1980 yo. Nan tan sila, lè Sida te fèk kòmanse kliyan ki tap rele nan telefòn epi ki tap vizite depatman lasante a te chaje ak laperèz, te prèt pou pran kriz de nè, te an kòlè, te santi yo pèdi lakat, te plen ak chagren.

Ring… ring…
"Bonjou. Se Lori kap pale la"
"Mwen tande ke genyen yon moun nan yon apatman nan bilding mwen rete a ki genyen maladi Sida. Tanpri ale fè ankèt pou mwen kapab kase kontra men te fè pou lwaye apatman mwen pou mwen soti al lòt kote"

Ring…ring…
"Bon apre midi. Kijan mwen kapab ede ou ?"
Oblije manadjè bilding la mete yon machin pou lave rad ak yon dryè separe pou moun ki gen Sida."

Ring... ring...
"Bonswa. Ki keksyon ou vle mande mwen?"
Si mwen ta boure yon ban papye klinèks nan bouch moun mwen an
afè a epi li pa senyen eske li san danje pou mwen bo avèk li ?"

Ring...ring...
"Bonjou. Ki sa ke ou vle nou fè?"
Devide ak netwaye tout pisin piblik yo epi mete yon pankat ki di ke
moun ki gen Sida pa kab benyen ladan yo,"

Ring...ring...
"Bon apremidi. Kijan mwen kapab ede ou ?"
" Eske ou kapab oblije menaj mwen fè tès Sida a epi ban mwen rezilta
tès li a ?"

Ring...ring...
"Bonswa. Ki sa ou vle?"
" Enspekte ak fè tès Sida pou tout doktè, pwofesè, travayè nan
restoran, estetisyèn ki ap fè zong moun, epi plake rezilta yo pou tout
moun kapab wè."

Ring...ring...
"Bonjou. Ou vle pote ki sa?"
" Men vle pote echantiyon san sou yon klinèks ak sou yon razwa
 pou yo fè yon tès Sida sou san a"

Ring...ring...
"Bonswa. Ou vle pou nou fè ki sa?"
"Eske nou pa kapab mete nan karantèn tout moun ki gen yon tès
Sida ki pozitif". Lori ak ekip ki okipe Sida te tèlman santi yo about
ke yo te vle rele anmwe.
"Rele, rele
Kite tout bagay sòti
Se bagay sa yo ke mwen pa bezwen
Vini non
Mwen ap pale ak ou
Vini non" 6

Moun yo te tankou ti bebe akokiye andedan vant manman yo tèlman yo tap krye ak laperèz.

Chak jou ekip yo te ap bay 10 rezilta tès ki te pozitif e menm plis ke 10, bagay sa te ap dechire kè si la ki te pi kourajèz nan travayè ki tap bay konsèy yo. Apre yo te fin bay rezilta tès yo sa ki te pi rèd la se te pou yo te eksplike moun nan ki te pozitif la ke pa te gen okenn tretman pou ofri li.

Lori sèt te oblige eksplike laverite a, oubyen bay rezilta yo kanmen lè ke moun yo pa te vle kwè sa yo te tande e ke yo te pito mete dwèt yo nan zorèy pou yo pa tande laverite a.

Ekip la te oblije negosye ak patyan yo pou mande yo lè yo ap antre nan rapò seksyèl pou yo fè aktivite seksyèl ki pwoteje kont maladi a. Genyen ki te tande. Genyen ki pa te tande ditou. Moun ki te genyen anpil posibilite pou trape maladi Sida akòz de jan yo te ap mennen vi yo, te kwè ke yo te gen chans epi ke ko yo te gen bon defans kont maladi a lè ke rezilta tès yo te negatif, men menm moun sa a yo te vini kwè ke yo te pèdi chans yo lè ke yo te retounen an apre pou yo fè tès epi yo te pozitif.

Menm kèk anplwaye kolèg li ki te ap travay bò kote Lori a te trape maladi Sida a.

Bagay ki te pi difisil epòk sa a se te prann patyans kont inyorans ak prejije

Kijan ke Lori ak ekip la te rive viv malgre tout lavalas inyorans ak prejije sa a. ?

PASKE YO TE RENMEN ZAF

SANTE PIBLIK AK TOUT KÈ YO ☼

Tear for fears " ki vle di an kreyol : moun ap krye paske yo gen laperèz nan kò yo, se yon gwoup ki jwe misik ki te fèt nan lane 1980
Gwoup misik sa a te van plis ke 21 milyon disk misik sou tout la tè a
6 se yon moso nan chante ke gwoup mizisyen tears for fears yo te fè ki rele " shout " (ki vle di rele an angle)

Triplets on a Plane

Written By Denise West, RD, LD

I, Denise, Director of the WIC and Nutrition Program in Miami, was sitting with my husband in the Miami International Airport waiting area for a flight to New York City. My attention was drawn to four adults hovering over three infants and lots of baby equipment. "Probably the parents and grandparents of triplets," I guessed. Pre-boarding was announced and I watched them work together to take all the babies and 'equipment' down the ramp. I was surprised to observe the grandparents exit the plane and thought, "Oh my, what a handful the three will be for those parents!"

As I took my seat, I realized I was behind this family; they had five of the six seats in the same row. The plane filled quickly and a young man in his twenties came to take the sixth seat. His face seemed unsure..."Would you like to trade seats with me?" Denise volunteered. He looked at the triplets, then at me, and responded, "YES, MA'AM. THANKS!"

Moving forward, I told the mother I would be glad to help if needed. She hesitated, and then asked if I would be willing to use a hand sanitizer. "Of course," I replied, as I took the plastic bottle from her and I gently rubbed the cleanser on. We took off and the time was quickly filled with holding babies, helping feed them and chatting. I learned the triplets were six months old and this was their first visit to meet their grandparents in NYC.

"You seem comfortable with children. What do you do?" the mom inquired.

"I work for the Miami-Dade County Health Department in a program called WIC – a nutrition program for Women, Infants and Children[10]."

The mom exclaimed, "I know all about WIC! The WIC staff has been amazingly helpful and so patient!" The story she told me is written below in her own words:

In January, I gave birth to triplets who arrived prematurely at 29 weeks. The social worker at the hospital recommended that I apply for WIC support, so I did. I am glad I did so, and I have been so grateful for the assistance I have received.

My journey with WIC began with a phone call. I ended up speaking with Madge Chin, who was understanding of my circumstances and assisted in arranging an appointment for me the following week. Next, I met Monique Legros, who has been patient in dealing with my case as my babies have had to change formulas several times for medical reasons. Monique is always pleasant to deal with and is genuinely concerned about the progress of my babies. Monique referred me to Lissa Nirenberg, the lactation specialist, because I was having some difficulties trying to breast feed my babies. Lissa arranged for lending me a breast pump and called me weekly to see how things were progressing and to answer any questions I had. Lissa even came to my home a couple of times in order to give me hands-on assistance in helping me with proper positioning and techniques to help the babies develop the skills they needed for nursing.

I have been very impressed with the professionalism of the above mentioned women. The two women who work at the counter of WIC (at Borinquen) have also always received me and others very respectfully, which I appreciate. I do not know their names, but they surely recognize mine as I have been a frequent visitor in their office.

So I extend my thanks to all the support my triplets and I have received from WIC.

Signed, An appreciative mom.

10 The Special Supplemental Nutrition Program for Women, Infants, and Children (WIC) is a Federal assistance program of the Food and Nutrition Service (FNS) of the United States Department of Agriculture (USDA) for healthcare and nutrition of low-income mothers and children under the age of five.
USDA's revamping of this program would provide more fruit, vegetables and whole grains to the diet while cutting back on the amount of dairy products. USDA has proposed these changes to reflect updates to the food pyramid introduced in 2005.
In many poor areas, "WIC stores" exist that only sell food for vouchers issued by the state WIC program, and do not accept any other form of payment. Wikipedia, 2007.

What an amazing coincidence to sit next to a family that had been so impacted by the WIC Program and had wonderful customer experience. I was so proud of the staff!

As I exited the plane with one of the babies and handed her into the arms of an anxiously awaiting grandmother, I was on cloud nine knowing that again our exceptional customer service made a significant difference in a family's life.

Trillizos en el Avión

Escrito por Denise West, RD, LD.

Yo, Denise, Directora de WIC y del Programa de Nutrición en Miami, estaba sentada con mi esposo en el salón de espera del Aeropuerto Internacional de Miami para viajar a la ciudad de Nueva York. Me llamaron la atención cuatro adultos cernidos sobre tres bebés y muchos equipos para bebés. "Probablemente los padres y abuelos de los trillizos," supuse. El pre-embarque fue anunciado y yo miré como se las arreglaban para llevar todos los bebés y el equipo por la rampa. Me sorprendí al ver a los abuelos salir del avión y pensé, ¡"Oh no, el problema que van a tener esos padres con los trillizos!" Cuando me senté, me di cuenta que estaba detrás de esta familia. Ellos tenían cinco de las seis sillas en la misma fila. El avión se lleno rápido y un joven que tenía alrededor de veinte años vino a sentarse en la sexta silla. Tenía en su cara una expresión de indecisión. ¿Quisieras cambiar de silla conmigo? Denise se ofreció. El miró a los trillizos, luego a mí, y respondió, "¡SI, SEÑORA. GRACIAS!"

De seguidas, le dije a la madre que yo estaría dispuesta a ayudarla si lo necesitaba. Ella dudó, y luego preguntó si yo estaba dispuesta a usar el gel de mano antibacterial. "Por supuesto," le dije, mientras ella me pasaba la botella de plástico y yo suavemente me frotaba las manos con el gel desinfectante. Despegamos y el tiempo pasó rápido entre cargar a los bebés, ayudar a alimentarlos y charlar. Me enteré que los trillizos tenían seis meses y este era su primer viaje a conocer a sus abuelos en la ciudad de Nueva York.

"Tú pareces sentirte cómoda con los niños. ¿Qué haces?" la mamá preguntó. Yo trabajo para el Departamento de Salud del Condado de Miami-Dade en el programa llamado WIC - un programa de nutrición para mujeres, bebés y niños[11]. La madre exclamó, ¡"Yo conozco todo sobre WIC! ¡El personal de WIC ha sido increíblemente servicial y pacientes!" La historia que ella me relató es la que está escrita abajo en sus propias palabras:

En Enero, yo di a luz a trillizos los cuales fueron prematuros de 29 semanas. La trabajadora social del hospital me recomendó que yo aplicara a la ayuda que provee WIC, y así lo hice. Y estoy contenta de haberlo hecho, y yo estoy tan agradecido por la ayuda que he recibido.

Mi travesía con WIC comenzó con una llamada telefónica. Terminé hablando con Madge Chin, quien comprendió mi circunstancia y me asistió en programar una cita para mí para la siguiente semana. Luego, conocí a Monique Legros, quien ha sido paciente al trabajar en mi caso, ya que mis bebés han tenido que cambiar de fórmula varias veces por razones médicas. Monique es una persona muy agradable de tratar y está verdaderamente preocupada acerca del progreso de mis bebés. Monique me refirió a Lissa Nirenberg, la especialista de lactancia, porque estaba teniendo dificultades para amamantar a mis bebés. Lissa se encargó de que se me prestara un sacaleches eléctrico y me llamaba semanalmente a fin de ver como progresaban las cosas y para contestar cualquier pregunta que yo tuviera. Lissa inclusive vino a mi casa un par de veces para darme asistencia práctica a fin de ayudarme con las posiciones y técnicas correctas para que los bebés pudieran desarrollar las habilidades necesarias para amamantar.

Yo he estado muy impresionada con el profesionalismo de las mujeres mencionadas anteriormente. Las dos mujeres que trabajan en el mostrador de WIC (en Borinquen) me han siempre recibido a mí y a otras muy respetuosamente, lo cual yo aprecio. Yo no conozco sus nombres, pero estoy segura que ellas reconocerían el mío, ya que he sido una visitadora frecuente de sus oficinas.

11 El Programa de Nutrición Suplementaria Especial para Mujeres, Bebés y Niños (WIC) es un programa de asistencia federal del Servicio de Nutrición y Alimentación (FNS) del Departamento de Agricultura de los Estados Unidos de Norte América (USDA) el cual provee asistencia sanitaria y nutrición a las madres y niños menores de cinco años de bajos ingresos económicos. La modernización de este programa por parte del USDA proveería más frutas, vegetales y alimentos integrales a la dieta mientras reduciría el monto de productos lácteos. USDA ha propuesto estos cambios a fin de reflejar los últimos cambios introducimos en la pirámide alimenticia del 2005. En muchas áreas pobres, existen "los almacenes de WIC" que solo venden alimentos a cambio de los vouchers emitidos por el programa estadal WIC, y no aceptan ninguna otra forma de pago. Wikipedia, 2007).

Por tanto yo le doy las gracias por todo el soporte que mis trillizos y yo hemos recibido de WIC.

Firmado, una madre agradecida.

Que increíble coincidencia el sentarme al lado de una familia que ha sido tan impactada por el programa WIC y que ha tenido una experiencia maravillosa como cliente. ¡Yo estaba tan orgullosa del personal!

Mientras salía del avión con uno de los bebés y se lo entregaba en los brazos a la abuela que ansiosamente aguardaba la llegada, yo estaba muy feliz que otra vez nuestro excepcional servicio al cliente hizo una diferencia significante en la vida de una familia. ☼

Twa Marasa
Nan Yon Avyon

Se Denise West, RD, LD ki ekri istwa sa a.

Mwen menm Denise, Direktè pwogram WIC ak Nitrisyon nan Miyami a, te chita ak mari mwen nan èpòt entènasyonal Miyami a, nou tap tann pou vol avyon ki pral New-York City a. Lè sa kat gran moun tap afere yo otou twa ti bebe ak yon bann ekipman pou ti bebe. "Petèt se te paran ak gran paran twa ti marasa." mwen te sipoze. Yo te fè anons pou moun komanse anbake nan avyon a, lè sa mwen wè yo tout mache ansanb pou mete ti bebe yo ak ekipman pou ti bebe yo nan ranp pou anbake avyon an. Mwen te sezi lè mwen te wè grann parann yo soti nan avyon a, epi mwen di tèt mwen" Woy! parann sa yo pral pran pa yo ak ti moun sa yo."

Pandan mwen tap chita nan plas mwen nan avyon a, mwen rann mwen kont ke mwen te chita dèyè fanmi a: yo te pran senk nan sis chèz ki te nan ranje chèz la pou yo chita. Avyon a tap plen byen vit, epi yon jen gason vent an te vin pou chita nan sizyème chèz la. Figi li te yon tijan pentade lè li tap gade chèz vid la boke fanmi ak ti bebe yo. " Eske ou vle chanje plas ak mwen " Denise te ofri li. Li gade twa marasa yo apre li gade mwen epi li reponn, "WI MADANM MÈSI ANPIL."

Mwen kontinye, mwen di manman an ke sa ta fè mwen plezi pou mwen ede li si li bezwen mwen. Li ezite, epi lè sa li mande mwen si mwen tap dakò pou mwen sèvi ak yon pwodwi pou touye jèm sou men moun (sanitizer) " Natirèlman, mwen te reponn li pandan ke mwen tap pran boutèy plastik la nan men li epi mwen tap fwote pwodwi a nan men mwen tou dousman. Avyon a vole, epi tan an te pase byen vit nan kenbe ti bebe, nan ba yo manje, epi nan bay odians. Mwen aprannn ke twa marasa yo te gen si mwa epi ke se te premye vizit yo pou al wè gran paran yo ki te rete nan New-York.

"Ou sanble ou a lèz ak ti moun, ki sa ke ou fè kòm travay?" manman ti moun yo te mande mwen. Mwen travay nan Depatman Lasante nan Miyami nan yon pwogram ki rele WIC –yon pwogram pou nitrisyon fanm, ti moun ak ti bebe[12]. Manman ti moun yo di'm, mwen konnen tout bagay sou WIC!" Jan anplwaye WIC yo te ede mwen te ekstraòdinè, epi yo te tèlman gen patyans. Istwa madanm nan te rakonte'm nan m'ap ekri li ak egzakteman mo li te di mwen yo.

Nan mwa Janvye mwen te akouche twa ti marasa ki te fèt avan tèm lè mwen te gen sèlman 29 semen ansent. Sosyal wokè nan lopital la te di mwen pou mwen aplike pou ke WIC kab ede mwen, kidonk mwen te fè sa. Mwen kontan ke mwen te fè sa epi mwen tèlman rekonesan pou jan ke yo te ede mwen.

Eksperyans mwen ak WIC konmanse ak yon kout fil. Mwen te pale ak Madge Chin, ki te konprann sitiyasyon mwen epi ki te fè yon randevou pou mwen nan semen ki te swiv apèl mwen a. Apre sa, mwen te rankontre ak Monique Legros, ki te pran anpil patyans ak ka mwen, paske ti bebe mwen yo te oblije chanje lèt yo bwè a plizyè fwa akòz de pwoblèm lasante. Monique toujou janti lè li ap bay sèvis epi li vrèman okipe li de kijan pwogrè ti bebe mwen yo te ye. Kòm mwen te gen difikilte nan eseye bay ti bebe mwen yo tete, Monique te voye mwen al wè Lissa Nirenberg ki se espesyalist pou ede moun ki ap bay ti moun tete. Lisa te fè yo prete mwen yon ponp pou rale lèt nan tete epi li te rele mwen nan telefòn chak semen pou wè kijan bagay yo tap mache epi tou pou li te kab reponn tout keksyon mwen yo.

Lissa te menm vizite mwen kèk fwa pou ede mwen, sitou pou li te montre mwen bon jan pozisyon pou mwen te mete ti moun yo

12 Pwogram espesyal pou ajoute sou nitrisyon fanm, ti moun ak ti bebe (WIC) se yon pwogram gouvènman federal nan pwogram pou manje ak sèvis nitrisyon ki rele Food an Nutrisyon Service (FNS) ki nan Depatman agrikilti (USDA) pou ede ameliore lasante ak nitrisyon manman ak ti moun ki genyen mwens ke senk lane e ki pa gen anpil mwayen. Lè USDA te pase men nan pwogram la, li te bay plis fwi, legim, ak sereal ki pa blanchi pou moun yo manje pandan ke li te wete sou kantite lèt ak pwoduyi lèt. USDA te fè chanjman sa yo pou ke li suiv chanjman na piramid sou zafè manje ke yo te mete deyò nan lane 2005.Nan anpil zòn malerèz boutik WIC la pou vann manje ak koupon ke pwogram WIC nan eta bay moun, boutik sa yo pa aksepte pou moun peye yo lòt jan ke ak koupon. (Se sa diktyonè ki rele Wikipedia di nan lane 2007)

prann tete a pou yo te byen devlope abilte pou byen rale lèt nan tete mwen.

Mwen te rete bouch be devan jan medam sa yo te fè travay yo byen, jan yo te fè profesyon yo chwazi a onè.

De medam ki travay sou kontwa WIC nan sant Borinquen la toujou resevwa mwen menm ak lòt klyan yo ak anpil koutwazi, se yon bagay mwen te apresye anpil. Mwen pa konnen non yo men yo byen rekonèt non pa mwen paske mwen te vizite biwo WIC la souvan.

Mwen ap remèsye nou pou tout sipò marasa mwen yo ak mwen te resevwa nan pwogram WIC la.

Se yon manman ki apresye tout sa yo fè pou li ki siyen anba sa ki ekri la.

Se yon chans ekstraòdinè ke mwen te ale chita bò kot yon fanmi ke pwogram WIC la te fè dibyen anpil e ki te gen yon si bèl eksperyans ak pwogram la. Mwen te fyè anpil de anplwaye WIC yo.

Lè mwen tap soti nan avyon a ak yon nan ti bebe yo epi mwen te lonje li bay grannn li ki tap tann li ak enpasyans. Mwen te ozanj paske mwen te konnen ke sèvis ekstraòdinè nou bay yo te pote anpil bon chanjman nan lavi yon fanmi.

Se Denise West, RD, LD ki ekri istwa sa a. ☀

Rocky Raccoon

The azure-blue summer sky was lined with feathery cirrus clouds, as Nancy, a five- year old blond-headed girl, was streaking across Naranja's Plants-Are-Us Nursery. She was looking at a burly raccoon named, "Rocky". Rocky Raccoon was chained to an olive tree.

As the girl reached over to pet the raccoon, the scared carnivore snarled his teeth at the child. However, the message did not register. As her hand inched closer to Rocky's mouth, Rocky's teeth sunk deep into the Nancy's left hand. Nancy's parents (Lil and Dan) heard their child's curdling howl. Her parents hurriedly drove their crying, bleeding child to their family doctor. They worried that Nancy would need to undergo a series of painful rabies vaccine shots. The physician taught the family about rabies[13].

The Doctor reported the bite to Health Department's Epidemiology Program. The family wanted the raccoon tested [14]so their child could forego the painful shots.

The telephone call came into the legal department, requesting a court order to search the property and seize the raccoon for testing. The Health Department attorney knew the routine; he drafted his

13 Rabies (Latin, rabies, "madness, rage, fury") is a viral zoonotic disease that causes acute encephalitis (inflammation of the brain) in mammals. In non-vaccinated humans, rabies is invariably fatal after neurological symptoms have developed, but prompt post-exposure vaccination may prevent the virus from progressing. Only six humans are known to have survived rabies after the onset of symptoms. There is only one known case of a person surviving rabies without treatment. Wikipedia, 2007.

14 Any mammal may become infected with the rabies virus and develop symptoms, including humans. Most animals can be infected by the virus and can transmit the disease to humans. Infected bats, raccoons, foxes, skunks, dogs or cats provide the greatest risk to humans.

lawsuit; he called the father of the girl to testify; he gathered the Health Department's veterinarian, Dr. John Black, and walked across the street to the court house. The attorney introduced himself to the Judge, who carefully listened to the victim's father, and the veterinarian about the transmission of rabies and the risk of death to the child.

The Judge also listened to the testimony of the owners of Ricky. But after hearing of the risk to the life of the five year old girl, the Judge ruled that the raccoon had to be tested.

With the order in hand, Dr. Black and the Attorney now had to coordinate seizure of raccoon with the police and County Animal Control.

Here was the game plan; we would all meet a block away from the nursery. On the way down, we met three Wild Life and Fish and Game Officers in their patrol car.

Here's the picture, one car with the Health Department Lawyer and Veterinarian, two animal control vehicles, one police car with two officers, one Wildlife vehicle with three Fish & Game Officers, for a total of five vehicles and ten Government officials, all for Rocky.

As we drive up to the property, we are met by an 80 year old man holding a Gideon Bible and wearing beached out overalls and a t-shirt emblazed with the logo of "Plants r Us" Nursery.

The lawyer handed the old timer the search and seizure warrant. The old timer looked at the ten government officials and in a slow southern drawl, inquired, "Why didn't you bring the Judge?"

We all laughed knowing it looked like an army had attacked the nursery but realizing that a five year old girl's life was on the line.

Rocky tested negative and the girl did not have to seek further medical intervention. ☼

El Mapache Rocky

E l cielo azul celeste de verano estaba trazado con emplumadas, blancas y finas nubes, mientras Nancy, una rubia niña de cinco años, estaba correteando en el Naranja's Plants-Are-Us Nursery. Ella estaba mirando a un fornido mapache llamado "Rocky". El mapache Rocky estaba encadenado a un árbol de olivo.

Mientras la niña se acercaba a acariciar al mapache, el asustado carnívoro le gruñó. Sin embargo, el mensaje no lo entendió. Mientras se acercaba a la boca de Rocky, los dientes de Rocky se clavaron profundamente en la mano izquierda de Nancy. Los padres de Nancy (Lil y Dan) oyeron los alaridos espeluznantes de la niña. Sus padres llevaron deprisa a la niña llorando y sangrando al médico de cabecera. Ellos estaban preocupados de que Nancy pudiera necesitar someterse a una serie de dolorosas vacunas contra la rabia. El médico instruyó a la familia acerca de la rabia.[15]

El Doctor reportó el mordisco al Programa de Epidemiología del Departamento de Salud. La familia quería que el mapache fuera examinado[16] a fin de que la niña pudiera evitar las dolorosas vacunas.

La llamada vino al Departamento Legal, pidiendo una orden

15 Rabia (Latín, rabies, "locura, cólera, furia") es una enfermedad viral que causa encefalitis aguda (inflamación del cerebro) en los mamíferos. El los seres humanos no vacunados, la rabia es invariablemente fatal después que los síntomas neurológicos se han desarrollado, pero la pronta vacunación prontamente después de la exposición puede prevenir que el virus progrese. Solo se conoce de seis personas que han sobrevivido la rabia después de que los síntomas se han manifestado. Solo se conoce de un caso en el cual una persona sobrevivió la rabia sin tratamiento. Wikipedia, 2007.

16 Cualquier mamífero puede infectarse con el virus de la rabia y desarrollar síntomas, incluyendo los seres humanos. La mayoría de los animales pueden ser infectados con el virus y pueden transmitir la enfermedad a los humanos. Los murciélagos, mapaches, zorros, zorrillos, perros y gatos infectados presentan el mayor riesgo a los humanos.

judicial a fin de registrar la propiedad y aprehender al mapache para examinarlo. El abogado del Departamento de Salud sabía el procedimiento a seguir: él redactó la demanda; llamó al padre de la niña a testificar; recogió al veterinario del Departamento de Salud, Dr. John Black, y cruzó la calle hacia el edificio de tribunales. El abogado se le introdujo al Juez, quien cuidadosamente oyó al padre de la víctima, y al veterinario acerca de la transmisión de la rabia y el riesgo de muerte para la niña. El Juez también oyó el testimonio de los dueños de Rocky. Pero después de oír los riesgos que tenía la vida de la niña de cinco años, el Juez dictaminó que el mapache debía ser examinado.

Con la orden en mano, el Doctor Black y el abogado ahora debían coordinar la aprehensión del mapache con la policía y la agencia de Control de Animal del Condado.

Estas eran las reglas del juego: todos nos reuniríamos a una cuadra del vivero. En la vía nos encontramos con tres funcionarios de la agencia de la Fauna, Especies Marinas y Cacería (Wild Life, Fish and Game) en sus patrullas.

Esta es la descripción de la situación: un carro con el abogado y veterinario del Departamento de Salud, dos vehículos de la agencia de Control de Animal, un carro de la policía con dos funcionarios, un vehículo de la agencia de la Fauna, Especies Marinas y Cacería, lo cual hacía un total de cinco vehículos y diez funcionarios del gobierno, todos por Rocky.

Mientras manejábamos a la propiedad, nos encontramos con un hombre de 80 años que tenía una Biblia de Gideon en la mano y usaba un mono decolorado y una camiseta con el logotipo de Plants-Are-Us nursery.

El abogado le entregó al anciano la orden de registro y aprehensión. El anciano miró a los diez funcionarios del gobierno y con un lento acento sureño preguntó, ¿Por qué no trajeron al Juez también?

Todos nos reímos de ver que parecíamos una armada atacando el vivero pero dándonos cuenta que la vida de una niña de cinco años estaba en peligro.

Los resultados de los exámenes realizados a Rocky fueron negativos y la niña no necesitó intervención médica adicional. ☼

Raton Laveur

Syèl ble nan sezon fè cho a te genyen kèk ti mak niyaj lapli ladan li jou sa a ke Nancy, yon ti fi ak cheve koulè bab mayi tap kouri nan pepinyè Narannja Plant Are Us la. Ti fi a tap gade yon raccoon byen kosto ki rele Rocky. Yo te mare raccoon nan nan yon pye zoliv.

Pandan ke ti moun nan tap proche pou li jwe ak raccoon la, zannimo a ki te pè ti fi a te soti dan li pou eseye mode ti moun nan. Malgre sa, ti fi a pa te konprann pou li kite bèt la an repo. Kòm ti fi a tap proche men li yon pous pi pre de bouch Rocky. Bèt la foure dan li byen fon nan men gòch Nancy. Paran Nancy yo (Lil ak Dan) tande pitit yo ki tap rele yon gwo rèl. Yo kouri ak ti moun ki tap rele epi tap senyen a, yo ale byen vit lakay doktè lafanmi a.Tèt yo te chaje de se ke Nancy ta pral oblije pran yon seri piki vaksen pou laraj ki bay anpil doulè. Doktè a te bay fanmi a enfòmasyon sou maladi laraj.12

Doktè a te rapote zafè mòde a bay pwogram ki reskonsab epidemi nan depatman lasante a. Fanmi ti moun nan te vle yo fè tès laraj 13 pou raccoon la pou wè si yo te kapab evite ke ti moun nan pran vaksen laraj yo ki fè moun soufri anpil.

Apèl telefòn nan te vini nan depatman ki okipe zafè la lwa a, paran yo tap mande tribinal lajistis pou li bay lapolis yon papye tenbre ak lòd pou al chèche ak sezi raccoon la pou fè teste li pou laraj. Avoka depatman lasante a te konnen sa li gen abitid fè ; li ekri papye pou rele mèt raccoon nan lajistis, li rele papa ti moun nan bou li vini sèvi temwen, li pase men li li prann doktè veterinè depatman lasante ki te doktè John Black, li janbe la ri pou li ale nan tribinal la. Avoka a prezante tèt li bay jij la, ki tande ak bon jan atansyon eksplikasyon papa ti moun nan ak doktè veterinè a te bay sou ki jan moun pran maladi laraj la epi tou danje ke ti moun nan tap trape maladi a epi mouri ak laraj la.

Jij la te tande temwanaj mèt Ricky yo tou. Men lè ke li tande te gen danje pou ti moun senk an a ta va mouri, li prann jijman pou fè raccoon la fè tès la.

Ak papye tenbre tribinal la nan men li Dr Black ak avoka a te ap koòdone ak lapolis ak biwo sèvis zannimo pou sezi raccoon la.

Men sa yo te planifye pou yo fè : tout ajans gouvnman yo tap rankontre nan yon blok de pepinyè a. Sou wout pou nou desan la, nou kontre ak twa ofisye biwo bèt sovaj pwason ak jibye ki te nan otomobil patwòl yo.

Men kijan sa tap pase: yon oto ak avoka epi veterinè depatman lasante a, de oto biwo sèvis zannimo, yon oto lapolis ak de ofisye, yon oto biwo bèt sovaj pwason ak jibye ak twa ofisye ladan li, rasanble ansanb te genyen senk otomobil ak dis ofisyèl gouvenman, tout sa pou ti Rocky.

Pandan nou tap konduyi sou pwopriyete a, nou rankontre ak yon gran moun 80 zan ki te kenbe yon Bib Gideon nan men li, li te abiye ak yon ovewòl blaze ak yon mayo ki te gen non pepinyè a " Plants R Us " make sou li.

Avoka a lonje papye tenbre tribinal ki bay lòd pou chèche ak sezi racoon la bali. Gran moun ansyen tan a gade dis ofisyèl gouvènman yo, epi ak pale trennen moun nan Sid yo li mande yo "Pouki sa nou pa te mennen jij la tou ? "

Nou tout te ap ri paske nou te konnen ke li te sanble ke yon lame te atake pepinyè a men sa pa te trakase nou paske sa ke nou te konnen se te ke la vi yon ti fi senk an te an danje.

Tès Rocky a te negatif, kidonk ti moun nan pa te bezwen ke doktè te fè anyen de plis pou li. ☼

11 Se yon chante nan " White " albòm mizik gwoup mizisyen Beatles yo

12 Laraj non an laten rabies " foli firyèz, se yon maladi ke yon viris bay moun ak zannimo, viris sa a lakòz ke sèvo moun nan genyen yon enflamasyon.Si yon moun trape viris laraj la epi li pa prann vaksen li ap mouri kan menm apre ke li gen siyn ke nè li atake..Men si moun ki an kontak ak viris laraj la resevwa vaksen sa ap anpeche viris la fè ravaj. Nan tout moun sou latè a se sèlman sis moun ki sove apre ke maladi laraj te komanse parèt nan kò yo. Gen sèlman yon sèl moun sou la tè a ki te sove san ke li pa te prann tretman pou maladi a.

13 Nenpòt ki zannimo ki pote pitit an dedan vant yo epi ki bayo tete, sa yo rele mamifè yo, kapab vini enfekte ak viris laraj la epi devlope siyn maladi a, moun kapab prann maladi a tou. Preske tout zannimo mamifè yo kapab enfekte ak viris si la a epi tou pase maladi a bay moun. Chòv sourit, raccoon, rena, skunk (putwa puyan), chen, chat se bèt ki pi gwo danje pou bay moun maladi laraj.

Twenty-One Reasons to Write Your "Healthy Story"

Last week, a Health Department employee stopped by our offices for a visit. She thanked us for writing our Healthy Stories, specifically, for Dr. Conti's story. She said, "I've had many health problems and was afraid go to the doctor. After reading 'Physician Heal Thyself' I went to my doctor. I'm finally taking care of myself."

A simple short story can make a difference.

Here are an additional twenty reasons to make a change in your life and maybe in someone else's.

1. We're the only Public Health Department story book in town.
2. Because we are going national.
3. Because we are on eleven sites on the World Wide Web.
4. Because we are found in libraries in all fifty states.
5. Writing can make sense of your life.
6. Writing is personally valuable, life enhancing and pleasurable.
7. Writing can heal the spirit and nurture the soul.
8. Write for self-discovery.
9. Write for publication.
10. Write for your friends and family.
11. Because you listen to the past, future, and present.
12. Because you were born with creative urges.
13. Because you need to be heard.
14. Because you are an observer.
15. Because you love the written word.
16. Because you understand imagery and dialogue.
17. Because writing is better than—you fill in the blank.
18. Because you like to confront your fears.
19. Because you are a risk taker.
20. Because you are brave.
21. Because you have story to tell.

How to Contact the Editors, Submit a Story or Order Additional Copies of Healthy Stories 2008

Perhaps you have experienced or know about a healthy tale that you would like to share in Healthy Stories 2009. Your stories don't have to be limited to happenings at a Health Department, as long as your narrative has a health-related theme. We are hoping to get one story from each of the fifty states. We would enjoy hearing from you. Along with your tale, just let us know how we can contact you in case we need to clarify any details.

We welcome your comments or suggestions about this book. You can write or e-mail us at the addresses shown below.

Need additional copies of this book for yourself or friends, if your bookstore or Amazon didn't stock enough copies, they should be able to obtain them for you. If you would rather order them yourself just make your request and mail $10.95 (shipping included) per book to the following address or e-mail:

Tracie Dickerson or Mort Laitner
Healthy Stories 2008
Legal/Contracts Division
Miami-Dade County Health Department
8323 NW 12 Street, Suite 214
Miami, Florida 33126

E-mail: tracie_dickerson@doh.state.fl.us
        or mort_laitner@doh.state.fl.us

About the Editors

MORT LAITNER

Mort Laitner has practiced law for 33 years. He commenced practicing Family Law with the Legal Aid Society of Baton Rouge, Louisiana. His next job was with Legal Services of Greater Miami where his unit handled approximately 600 cases a year.

Since 1977, he has been the chief legal counsel for the Miami-Dade County Public Health Unit, where he specializes in public health law.

Mort has taught at the University of Miami, School of Medicine, St. Thomas University, and Miami-Dade College. He has lectured throughout Florida and Georgia on public health issues.

He has handled high-profile cases which received coverage on the CBS Nightly News, Life Magazine, Money Magazine and the New York Times. He has produced and directed Pandemic, an avian influenza film.

He is the author or co-author of seven books:

- Analytical Approach For the Preparation of the Louisiana Bar Examination
- Les Cartes De Baton Rouge
- Quarantine Preparing for the Attack Small Pox: Field Exercises A how to Manual for a Beginner's Level Field Exercises
- SARS: A Quarantine and Isolation Manual for Severe Acute Respiratory Syndrome
- It is Just a Matter of Time, Recommendations that can Save Your Life
- Healthy Stories 2007
- How to Create a Public Health Film Festival

Mort lives with his wife, Shelley, and has raised three sons, Jason, Travis, and Blake.

MICHAEL COVER

Michael Cover joined public service from private legal practice where he specialized in commercial and real estate litigation. As a private litigator, Mr. Cover fought hard for the rights of tenants in commercial landlord-tenant disputes, protected small businessmen against unscrupulous enterprises, and defended homeowners preyed upon by dishonest construction contractors after Hurricane Andrew.

Mr. Cover graduated from the University of Miami School of Law in 1994. At Miami, Mr. Cover focused on environmental and ocean law studies. He clerked for noted ocean law authority, Pr. Thomas Clingan. He interned with the Wilderness Society, where he was tutored by Jim Webb, well-known Everglades preservationist.

Michael Cover's interest in the environment precedes his legal career. As a journalist with a Miami-area daily, Mr. Cover covered a variety of "beats," but favored matters relating to preserving South Florida's unique ecology. During his career in public relations, Mr. Cover developed important exposure for Florida Keys environmental issues, specifically water quality and land use.

He began work for the Department of Children and Family Services, District 11, in July 1996, where he handled the Department's appellate practice and contributed in various areas of litigation practice, including economic services, dependency and guardianship. Since joining the Miami-Dade County Health Department in July 1997, Mr. Cover has acted as Associate for Chief Legal Counsel Mort R. Laitner, and is responsible for all facets of health-related and administrative law. Because of his background, he has placed significant emphasis on addressing environmental health issues.

HEATHER BEATON

Heather L. Beaton was born in Miami, Florida. After graduating from Florida State University in 1999, Heather attended the University of Florida, Levin College of Law. She graduated with her Juris Doctorate in May 2002 with honors. Heather is a member of the Florida Bar. She currently works at the Miami-Dade County Health Department as an attorney, overseeing all of the Agency's contracts. Heather lives with her husband, Marcos, her daughter, Kaitlyn, and a very large Boston Terrier, Blackjack.

J.D. SHINGLES

J.D. Shingles is originally from rural southwest Georgia. He moved to Miami in 1982 to work for the Grand Union Company, a grocery retailer, and Miami has since been his home. He currently works for the Miami-Dade County Health Department as a Contract Manager. He received his Bachelor's degree in Business Administration, Management from the Fort Valley State University (College). He volunteers at the Sant La Haitian Community Center as a Tax Preparer; Guardian Ad Litem; enjoys watching a good movie, mentoring, reading, fishing and traveling, whenever time permits. He is also an active member of Phi Beta Sigma Fraternity, Inc., Theta Rho Sigma Chapter.

NINFA URDANETA

Ninfa Urdaneta is an attorney licensed to practice in the State of Florida and Venezuela. Originally from Maracaibo, Venezuela, she moved to the United States were she got married and has an adorable baby boy with another on the way. She currently works for the Legal Department/Contracts Division for the Miami-Dade County Health Department. Through her experience in the private and governmental sectors, she has also worked for law firms, corporations and for the Venezuelan Supreme Court of Justice.

TRACIE L. DICKERSON

Tracie L. Dickerson was born in Galveston, Texas. In May of 2000, Tracie received her Bachelor of Science in Maritime Administration form Texas A&M University. She continued her education at the University of Miami's School of Law, and graduated with her Juris Doctor in May of 2003. Tracie was an associate at a law firm specializing in civil rights litigation prior to her employment with the Miami-Dade County Health Department. Tracie is a member of the Florida Bar, and is a member of the U.S. District Courts for the Southern, Middle and Northern Districts of Florida and the Southern and Northern Districts of Texas. Tracie has recently begun a new endeavor and is in her second year of the Masters Program for Public Health at Florida International University. Tracie has also published articles in the South Florida History Magazine, and at poetry.com and helium.com. When she is not traveling, Tracie enjoys spending her evenings with her friends and her two "puppies", Heidi and Austin.

AMY TEJIRIAN

Amy Tejirian is originally from Calgary, Alberta, Canada. She received her Bachelor's degree in Communication and French from the University of California at Santa Barbara. She was a kindergarten teacher for the Los Angeles Unified School District for a year. She continued her studies at the University of Miami School of Law where she received a Juris Doctorate. Amy is a member of the both Florida and California Bars. She enjoys working at the Miami-Dade County Health Department Legal/Contracts Division for over three years. Currently, she is earning a Certificate of Public Health from the University of Florida. She speaks French and Armenian fluently. On her free time, Amy likes to travel, go the beach and attend Florida Panthers games, although her hockey favorite team is the Calgary Flames.

FREDERICK VILLARI

Frederick Villari was born in Medfield, Massachusetts. He attended University of Miami for his undergraduate degree in Business Law and History. He continued his education at Rodger Williams University School of Law and received his Juris Doctor. After passing the Florida Bar he went on to become an Assistant Attorney General for the Office of the Attorney General under Charlie Crist. He then went on to work as an assistant state attorney under Katherine Fernandez-Rundle in Miami-Dade County. He has found his home and family working for the Legal Department of the Miami-Dade County Health Department. He is currently licensed to practice law in Florida and the District of Columbia. Frederick is married to Francesca and they have a beautiful baby boy named Frederick Joseph Villari, IV.